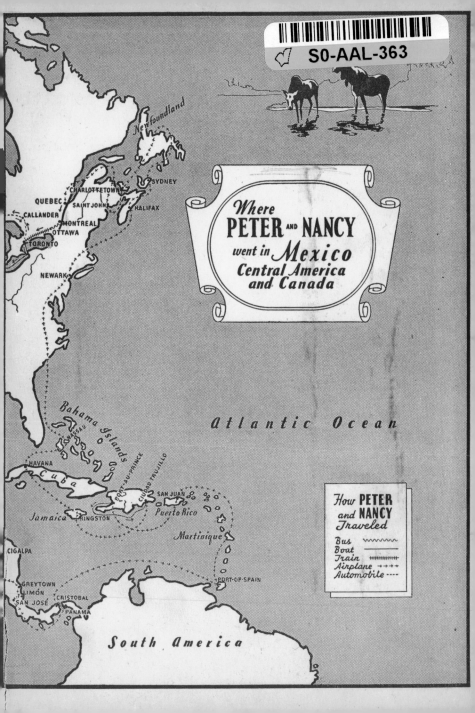

Where PETER AND NANCY went in Mexico Central America and Canada

Newfoundland

CHARLOTTETOWN
SYDNEY
QUEBEC
SAINT JOHN
CALLANDER
HALIFAX
MONTREAL
OTTAWA
TORONTO

NEWARK

Atlantic Ocean

Bahama Islands
NASSAU

HAVANA
Cuba
PORT-AU-PRINCE
CIUDAD TRUJILLO
SAN JUAN
Puerto Rico
Jamaica KINGSTON

Martinique

CIGALPA

GREYTOWN
LIMÓN
CRISTOBAL
SAN JOSÉ
PANAMA

PORT-OF-SPAIN

South America

How PETER and NANCY Traveled

Bus ～～～～
Boat
Train ┼┼┼┼┼┼
Airplane ＋＋＋＋
Automobile ----

PETER *and* NANCY *in* MEXICO

CENTRAL AMERICA, WEST INDIES, *and* CANADA

BY

MILDRED HOUGHTON COMFORT

Author of Peter and Nancy in the United States and Alaska
Peter and Nancy in South America
Peter and Nancy in Australia
Peter and Nancy in Europe
Peter and Nancy in Africa
Peter and Nancy in Asia

BECKLEY-CARDY COMPANY
CHICAGO

TO CEONE

CONTENTS

3

LIST OF
FULL-PAGE ILLUSTRATIONS

TO ALL OF YOU WHO ARE
GOOD NEIGHBORS

NEARLY everybody has at least one good neighbor, and truly fortunate people sometimes have two. Uncle Sam is one of these very fortunate people.

Peter and Nancy had always been fond of their rural neighbors, but, when they found they were going to visit their foreign neighbors, they were so happy and excited that they wished they could take all their friends on the journey. They wanted the children they knew and also the children they wished they knew.

Won't you come with them to visit the sunny, romantic neighbor on the south whose name is Mexico? And then, won't you go on with Peter and Nancy into Canada, the beautiful rich neighbor on the north?

The palms of Mexico and the evergreens of Canada are as different as the peoples and the customs of the countries. You'll travel by car and train and boat; and whenever you need to make a long, fast jump, Jimmy Dustin will be there with his plane.

The old car, with Uncle Lee at the wheel, is ready and waiting. Climb right in. You're most welcome!

THE AUTHOR

PETER AND NANCY IN MEXICO CENTRAL AMERICA AND CANADA

VISITING THE NEIGHBORS

IT WAS an exciting and an appropriate way to start the New Year. Mr. Lee MacLaren, that globe-trotting uncle who had taken his nephew, Peter, and his niece, Nancy, on so many wonderful trips, proposed the new journey at the close of the family dinner. He had come to the MacLaren farm in Minnesota for the holidays, and to enjoy the kind of plum pudding that only Mrs. MacLaren could make.

"The New Year," he announced to the assembled relatives, "is the proper time to call on the neighbors." Then, quite as though he were saying, "Let's run over and see the Browns," he suggested, "Let's take a trip to Mexico and then to Canada! What do you say, Peter? And you, Nancy?"

"Oh, Uncle Lee!" Peter jumped to his feet shouting, while Nancy gazed steadily at her uncle, her gray eyes shining.

Three days later Uncle Lee MacLaren bundled his charges into his car and headed southward with them. All three were bronzed from their long trip to Australia. Uncle Lee was

thinner, but his blue eyes were alight at the
prospect of more adventure. Peter had shot up
to a lanky height, but he was hard and firm of
muscle. Nancy had become almost a young lady.
Her smile was eager as she met Peter's grin.
"A visit to the neighbors!" she exulted.

The trip south was rapid, with mere glimpses
of Minnesota clad in its blanket of snow.

There was a succession of pictures, etched
clearly and vividly, which would long be remembered. Cattle and hogs feeding on cornstalks
in Iowa, or huddled together to escape the wintry
blasts! Drifting roads where their car slowly
followed a snowplow! Cozy warmth where Uncle
Lee decided on a brief rest in Des Moines! Running out of an Iowa snowstorm into sleet in
northern Missouri and having to scrape the freez-
ing moisture off the windshield!

A night at Kansas City! Off in the early morning! Through western Missouri, seeing great
peach and apple orchards! Then the foothills of
the Ozarks! Barefoot children playing in the
sun! Negro mammies washing clothes in a big
iron kettle in the yard! Derricks in the oil fields
of Oklahoma and Texas!

A night at Dallas! Peter and Nancy wishing
they might stop at San Antonio for a view of
the Alamo! Passing winter gardens and grape-
fruit groves!

Laredo, the Texas border town, looked more
Mexican than American. At least half the peo-

ple on the streets had black hair and brownish
skin. The signs in the store windows were in
Spanish. At the United States Post Office, where
the MacLarens received mail from home, the
clerks spoke Spanish much better than they did
English. The city was full of beautiful homes
showing the influence of Spanish architecture,
with their pink, orange, blue, and lavender walls,
and their gaily flowering patios, the delightful
garden squares around which the homes were
built, and where the women and children usually
spent the day. Peter had once read a definition
of a patio that he often quoted: A Spanish house
wrapped around the yard, instead of a yard
wrapped around the house.

Plazas, too, delighted Peter, for they were
important parks, beautiful with flowers and trees
and fountains. Around them the life of the town
revolved. In the evening the band played, and
everybody strolled about to enjoy the music and
to visit with friends and neighbors.

There were two Laredos, Peter and Nancy
knew. There was this Laredo in Texas and
another Laredo across the river, known as New
Laredo, or Nuevo Laredo. The MacLarens, after
resting for a night, repacked their luggage for
a trip into Mexico.

Peter and Nancy were impressed by the fact
that they were about to cross an international
border, but the dark-eyed children playing near
the bridge of the historic Rio Grande River ac-

James Sawders

THE BOUNDARY MARKER

cepted the wonder of living on the border as a matter of course.

Uncle Lee objected to a sticker, printed TOUR-IST, on his car. It had a hands-across-the-border motif which Nancy declared to be intriguing.

"We're not tourists, we're geographers!" Uncle Lee explained to the swarthy young man who had applied the sticker.

A grin was the only answer.

"Uncle Lee, please let Nancy and me walk across the bridge into Mexico," Peter begged.

"We want to examine the detachable aluminum railing. You said it was the only one in the world. There's a whole crowd from the school going over."

"All right," Uncle Lee agreed. "You know we don't have to have passports. I've got our tourist cards which permit us to travel in Mexico for six months. Our baggage has been inspected, and I've paid the duty on the car. There is nothing more to detain us."

Nancy was more quiet than Peter as the two started across the bridge. The Mexicans called this the "Wild River of the North," but there seemed to be nothing wild about it. It was a sluggish, brownish stream with thirsty-looking banks. As far as Nancy could see, there was nothing but rough, barren country. The river boasted few boats, no mill wheels, and, as Uncle Lee said later, no fish to speak of.

"Well, it's good as a boundary." Nancy spoke her thoughts aloud. Then she realized that the river wasn't even a good boundary because it twisted and turned too much. The boundary that it outlined was close to seven hundred miles as the crow flies. Uncle Lee had told about the commission in Washington that had to keep the farmers along the river from changing nationality every time the river took a new twist or turn.

Peter stopped at the middle of the bridge to look at the boundary marker. Its silver sides

bore the coats of arms of the United States and
of Mexico. Nancy stood beside her brother.
"I think I like our eagle better," she remarked.
"Theirs is perched on a spiny cactus and holds
a rattlesnake. But I suppose cactus and snakes
are typical of the country. What do you think of
the Rio Grande, Peter? Disappointed?"

"I should say not!" Peter's blue eyes shone like
the smiling Mexican sky. "It's an exciting river!
Think of the bandits and cattle thieves that wade
through its shallows or splash across it on their
horses! Think of the Mexican immigrants that
steal across it at night through some new turn
of the river! Government officials can't guard
every inch. Then there's the other side."

"Other side of the river, or other side of the
picture?" Nancy teased.

"Picture, if you choose to call it that," Peter
explained with dignity. "Every single year we
have the help of forty thousand Mexican workers,
crossing the border to work. They don't mind
manual labor. They pick cotton, repair railways, help in the oil industry. And we supply
a good deal of the food and clothing that Mexico
uses. In another minute we'll be in Mexico.
There's Nuevo Laredo ahead. Let's race for it."

At that moment Uncle Lee's car came alongside, and Uncle Lee insisted that Peter and Nancy
get into the back seat and ride.

They were amazed at the contrast between
the prosperous Laredo in Texas and this Nuevo

James Sawders

THE CUSTOMHOUSE IN NUEVO LAREDO

Laredo just across the river in Mexico. Paved
streets were few, and Uncle Lee's car stirred
the deep dust that rose to envelop it.

There were a few modern buildings in the
town including a hotel, but the homes could not
compare with the gay stucco houses of Laredo.

Nancy coughed in the dusty air. Through the
brownish fog of it she saw peddlers in broad-
brimmed hats and shabby, loose garments selling
candy, fruits, and biscuits. Once, when the car
slowed, a beggar besought Uncle Lee for some
coins. He was rewarded, whereupon other beg-
gars joined in a hue and cry.

To escape them Uncle Lee drove the car down

a street to the river's edge where women were beating clothes on the rocks.

"The Mexican washboard!" Peter exclaimed.

Uncle Lee turned the car back uptown and followed in the wake of the one tiny, rough-riding streetcar to the railway station. It was a small wooden building, constructed in Spanish style. But the railway employees outdid themselves to be resplendent. Their uniforms were handsome, and all their acts were executed with a flourish.

An American train arrived from San Antonio, a fine train such as Peter and Nancy were accustomed to ride on back home. But before it left the station second-class cars were coupled to it. Uncle Lee said fares were very low in these cars, and he secured permission for Peter and Nancy to inspect one.

The car had wooden-slat benches. There were lengthwise benches running along the sides of the car. In the middle were ten pairs of seats, back to back. Peter and Nancy tried the middle seats and thought it would be fun to go down to Mexico City by rail if only Uncle Lee had not decided to drive.

"All Mexican trains burn oil," Uncle Lee said. "You'd have no trouble on this train from soot or cinders. But there would be plenty of smoke."

"From what?" Nancy asked as Uncle Lee ushered her and Peter out of the car.

"From the passengers," Uncle Lee replied.

"Both the men and the women smoke a great deal, and the tobacco isn't always a mild variety."

"There aren't many railways in Mexico, are there, Uncle Lee?" Peter inquired. "I mean American railways."

The MacLarens were back on the platform again, and crowds were arriving. Uncle Lee chatted on, "The only American railway now in Mexico is the Southern Pacific that runs down the west side of Mexico to Guadalajara, second largest city in Mexico. Almost all the other railways are now combined under the National Railways of México and are run by Mexicans. There is really a very efficient network of railways across the country, as you will see.... Well, let's get started. It's a scant 150 miles to Monterrey, and we'll make it before dinner."

Uncle Lee took out his watch. One of the railway officials had come out on the platform, and Uncle Lee asked, "May I have the correct time, please?"

"Indeed, yes, sir," the official replied. "It is now precisely fifteen o'clock."

Peter grinned significantly at Nancy.

Uncle Lee seemed not in the least perturbed. He set his watch as Peter and Nancy stared. The hands told them it was exactly three o'clock.

"Code?" Peter inquired amusedly.

"Not at all," Uncle Lee spoke briskly. "It's a very sensible system. No question here as to whether or not a train is coming in at two in the morning or two in the afternoon. These sane Mexicans begin their counting at twelve o'clock midnight and keep right on counting up to twenty-four o'clock. It avoids confusion. Over the radio both times are given. An announcer will say, 'It is precisely 15 o'clock or 3 P. M.' "

Back in the car once more, the MacLarens said good-by to Nuevo Laredo.

The road was surprisingly good, with few crooks and turns. Part of it, Uncle Lee said, was claimed by the Mexicans to be the longest beeline stretch of motor highway in the world. On either side there was nothing but dusty brown plains dotted with mesquite shrubs, cactus, and other thorny plants.

The sun was a warm gold, and the sand seemed bathed in light. The air was balmy.

"I wish we could send some of this heat up to Minnesota," Peter remarked.

Nancy squirmed in her heavy wool suit.

"Before we leave Mexico," she remarked, "we'll be wishing that Minnesota would send a few snowflakes down here."

CLIMBING SOUTHWARD

IN THE slanting rays of the sun the desert took on a new beauty. Already the Mac-Larens felt the fascination of the brown, dusty plains with their odd, thorny vegetation and scattered Indian huts.

The blur on the sky line became the Sierra Madre range of mountains. In the midst of the brown plains appeared the town of Monterrey against a saddle-shaped mountain.

Uncle Lee remarked that Monterrey was often called the Pittsburgh of Mexico because of its smelters, its foundries, and its factories. He grumbled a little bit because, so he said, Americans who ran down to Monterrey for a gala time, had made it an expensive town for tourists.

Nancy exclaimed over the flat-roofed houses of Moorish-Spanish architecture. With their varied colors they seemed to fit into the landscape.

Because the big hotels were so expensive Uncle Lee drove his car into the outskirts of the town. At a roadside inn the MacLarens were served a dinner of American food, but Uncle Lee ordered a side dish of *chili con carne,* a peppery dish of meat served with beans, which Peter and Nancy tasted gingerly.

In the evening the MacLarens drove about the town. Uncle Lee pointed out buildings that looked

Ewing Galloway

AN INDIAN FAMILY AT HOME

as though they might have been built by the exploring Spaniards when they founded the city about 1560. Nancy loved the story of the young daughter of the conqueror, Montezuma, who came as an invalid to Monterrey to enjoy its sunny climate and its natural hot springs, and later returned home well and happy.

Early next morning the MacLarens drove out of Monterrey. In great fields men were cutting sugar cane.

"Seems funny, cutting sugar cane in January," Peter remarked, "when our fields back home are covered with snow."

Patches of different kinds of vegetation seemed

James Sawders

A SUBSTITUTE FOR MOTOR POWER

to run in series. There would appear a long field of sugar cane, then sandy desert with low, fat-leaved cactus and mesquite, followed by more sugar cane.

Before long Peter and Nancy saw their first palms in Mexico. They were short, stubby palms, but they sprouted big clusters of white bells.

Twenty-one miles south of Monterrey Uncle Lee turned the car into a side road, a bumpety-bumpety road, as Nancy described it. They passed a group of natives who were loading a truck that most people would have discarded. The motor was gone. As a substitute for motor power, two mules were hitched to the body of the truck.

"It wouldn't take long to wear out a car on roads like these," commented Uncle Lee.

Half an hour later the MacLarens drove into the lovely estate known as the Plantation of the Beautiful View.

The American friend who ran the plantation welcomed Uncle Lee's party with a hospitality that warmed their hearts. While the cook prepared lunch for them, the MacLarens wandered through the orchard. Mounds of oranges had been piled under the trees, and Uncle Lee observed, "We're welcome to all we can eat."

Eating the juicy, delicious oranges, Peter and Nancy followed Uncle Lee into a little canyon in which grew immense elephant-ear ferns and other tropical plants. The children were so greatly impressed with the big leaves that they did not notice the lovely scene ahead until Uncle Lee shouted, "There's Horsetail Waterfall!"

The little waterfall pitched down from the *mesa* above into a pool beneath.

"It does look like the silvery tail of a gray horse," Peter declared.

After lunch the MacLarens drove back to the highway and continued their journey southward. Now higher palms appeared. Against the sky line rose organ cacti, looking very much like the pipes of an organ. The cacti were rough and spiny. Near the top were short, thick little arms.

"It's 180 miles from Monterrey to Ciudad Victoria," Uncle Lee observed.

Ewing Galloway

AN ORGAN CACTUS PLANT

"And a good road all the way!" Peter exclaimed.

"It's known as the Pan-American Highway, isn't it, Uncle Lee?" Nancy asked. "At school

James Sawders

THE PAN-AMERICAN HIGHWAY

we learned that 'pan' is from the Greek and means *all*. This highway extends through America and makes us feel as though we were just going to visit a neighbor. It goes all the way to Mexico City, doesn't it, Uncle Lee?"

"Yes," Uncle Lee responded, "and when it is finally completed it will reach from Mexico to Alaska. The last time I was here this road was being blasted out and filled with crushed stone. There seemed to be an endless row of Indians working on it to make it smooth for the *gringos*, or tourists."

"Gringos!" Peter laughed. "I suppose I'm a gringo. Nancy, you're a gringo, too!"

"Uncle Lee, is that a Mexican word?" Nancy asked.

"No. It's a coined word," Uncle Lee explained. "A nickname! Mexicans used to use it in an insulting manner, but nowadays it's more often a term of affection than otherwise. Some people think the name originated during our war with Mexico in 1848."

"How?" Peter asked eagerly.

"American soldiers at that time frequently sang one of Robert Burns' poems. It began, 'Green grow the rushes, O.' Well, out of that phrase 'green grow' came the word gringo. 'Believe it or not!' "

The road continued to climb, winding in and out of mountain passes. The cornfields in small patches gave way to sand and mesquite.

"The mountains seem to be closing in on us," Peter decided. "I'm glad it isn't Mexican bandits. Uncle Lee, the engine is beginning to feel the altitude."

"Saltillo ahead," said Uncle Lee as he frowned at the sputtering engine. "I'm going to leave the car there anyway and have it driven into Mexico City. We'll go by train."

The car limped into a garage, and the Mac-Larens rushed to the railway station in a cab. There they learned that a train did not leave until almost midnight.

Peter and Nancy strolled eagerly about the quaint little town. It was very cool and invigor-

James Sawders

DONKEYS CARRYING FODDER

ating, and the big market was splashed with
the color of oranges and bananas and papayas.
Dust rose about the legs of donkeys laden with
produce, but that was not surprising since January was the driest month of the year in Mexico.
Moreover, Saltillo was a mile high and in a
fruit-producing area.

It was impossible to secure space in the first-
class, air-cooled cars. But that fact did not dis-
courage Uncle Lee. It would be an experience for
Peter and Nancy to ride in the second-class cars;

besides, it would save money. There would be more *pesos* to spend in Mexico City.

The car appeared to be crowded to capacity as the MacLarens entered it, for the long benches, as well as the back-to-back seats in the middle, were occupied. However, a pretty, black-haired woman placed one of her sleeping children on the floor and made room for Nancy. Some boys moved over to make room for Peter on the long bench, and Uncle Lee was offered space between two somber Indians who were smoking very black cigars. There was an air of good-natured hospitality, and the MacLarens were made to feel very welcome.

Men standing near the doors wore their *sombreros*, those broad-brimmed hats worn by every native or adopted Mexican. Others in the car dozed with their sombreros tilted down over their dark faces, or sliding off their laps onto the floor.

As the train pulled out, a finely dressed Mexican angrily pushed his way into the car. But he was somewhat mollified at the sight of the American travelers, who also had failed to secure accommodations in the first-class cars.

Neither Peter nor Nancy could take their eyes off this picturesque person with flashing dark eyes, gleaming white teeth, handsome sombrero, rich jacket, and tight trousers. Most of the sombreros in the second-class car were of coarse straw or thick felt, but every one was decorated with colored tape and embroidery. The hat of the important personage was trimmed with much gleaming silver and must have been very heavy to wear.

The wealthy Mexican's jacket reached only to his waist and was ornate with much embroidery and many buttons. The shirt, without collar or necktie, was a bright blue. About his slim waist he had wound a bright red sash of silk. The tight trousers were decorated with rows of buttons from waist to ankles. The heels of his shoes were much higher than Uncle Lee's.

Uncle Lee, who managed finally to secure a seat near Peter and Nancy, explained that it was not unusual for a Mexican to pay a hundred dollars or more for a sombrero.

As the train climbed, Nancy observed that most of the men in the car wore pieces of cowhide tied with leather strings in place of shoes.

"*Guaraches,*" Uncle Lee explained. "And those blankets with the slits through which to stick their heads are *ponchos*. They take the place of overcoats and are sometimes used as saddles or bedding."

"Don't the women wear hats?" Nancy asked, her gaze traveling over the dark, shining feminine heads with blue-black hair parted and coiled at the nape of the neck in every case. The children's heads of hair were like black satin caps.

"The women wear the *rebozo*, a combination shawl and head wrap," Uncle Lee explained. "Their skirts are always full and long, and they

James Sawders

SPINNING WOOL FOR SERAPES

seldom wear shoes. Some wear sandals while
traveling, but in the villages they go barefoot.
Why Mexican men and boys wear shoes while
girls and women go barefoot I do not know."

The farther south the train went, the cooler
the night air became because of the altitude. The
good-natured crowd settled down in *serapes*, and
the MacLarens got out their coats.

Toward daylight Uncle Lee remarked that they
were crossing the Tropic of Cancer into the Tor-
rid Zone, but neither Peter nor Nancy heard.

Kindly Mexicans had wrapped them in serapes, and they were sleeping in warmth and comfort. When they did awaken, the sun was up, and the bare, brown landscape was flying by. Peter and Nancy wanted to know what had become of the mountains. Uncle Lee explained that the reason they couldn't see the mountains was because they were on top of them.

Southward from Saltillo the train had run through Catorce, a rocky little town near the richest silver mines in Mexico. Now it was speeding across miles of broad plains. Field after field of maguey appeared.

Bright eyes began to smile. Travelers gathered up luggage.

"We're coming into San Luis Potosí," Uncle Lee said.

The well-dressed Mexican beamed.

"San Luis Potosí!" He rolled the words on his tongue. "It is one of the most modern cities of Mexico. It has a perfect climate. It has the most beautiful cathedral. Its people are very kind. It is the capital of the state of San Luis Potosí which was the first state in Mexico to pass laws in favor of the working classes such as the people you see in this car."

Several Mexicans laughed good-naturedly.

"Let the Americans judge for themselves," suggested an old Mexican. "I have been in their Texas. They will be surprised and pleased with our San Luis Potosí."

LIFE IN THE HIGHLANDS

WHEN they stood upon the platform at San Luis Potosí, Peter and Nancy were surprised to find that they were perfectly comfortable in their coats. The air was cold and clear. Uncle Lee said that on his last visit, it had been rainy and that he had had to walk or stay in bed in order to keep warm. Now the winter sun shone pleasantly.

The station was lively with men and boys begging for a chance to carry luggage. They all wore tight trousers, short jackets, and collarless shirts. In addition, nearly every one had slipped a serape over his head for warmth and had tied guaraches on his feet for protection. Uncle Lee picked two shabby youths to carry the hand luggage.

"I wonder what a breakfast here would be like," Peter hinted.

"Let's find out," Uncle Lee agreed.

At a small table in a dark little restaurant the three travelers were soon enjoying hot *tortillas* and delicious chocolate. There was a hint of vanilla and spice in the chocolate, and it was stirred with a swizzle stick, Uncle Lee explained.

"Mexican chocolate is always good," he declared. "Now we'll go over to a real Mexican hotel and get some rest. Tomorrow is Saturday,

market day, and I want you to feel refreshed in
order to enjoy it."

The hotel proved to be even more simple than
Uncle Lee had implied it might be. There was no
plumbing, and Nancy had to ask for a pitcher
of water and a bowl. There was no furniture
in her room except a hard bed, a table, and a
chair. Nancy lay down on the bed with her coat
over her and almost immediately fell asleep. She
did not awaken until Uncle Lee and Peter
pounded on her door, shouting, "Time for dinner!"

The dinner in the hotel was a regular Mexican meal, according to Uncle Lee. There was
a thin soup, some boiled beef and watery vegetables served with hot tortillas and peppers.
Then followed some rice and chili con carne. For
dessert Peter and Nancy ate oranges, and Uncle
Lee drank the blackest coffee they had ever seen.

Strolling along the cobbled streets, the Mac-
Larens viewed many well-constructed buildings,
including a really interesting cathedral.

"There seem to be two towers on all Mexican
churches," Nancy observed. "And they are
nearly always whitewashed and then decorated
with royal blue and bits of gilt."

"I like the idea of two towers," Peter declared.
"Some churches are built in lonely places. One
tower would look sad from lack of companion-
ship."

"I like that idea, Peter," Nancy conceded.
"Yes, two towers can keep each other company."

As the MacLarens approached some of the residences, they saw that nearly every house was built around a garden patio, even the most crumbly adobe home. Nancy stopped to peek in at a girl of her own age who was sweeping the patio of her home with a twig broom.

The little girl glanced up shyly and invited the strangers to look at her garden. She and Uncle Lee chatted in Spanish while Peter and Nancy admired the blooming plants. Magenta bougainvillea climbed a wall against which poinsettias were still in bloom. Uncle Lee said the poinsettias were called *noches buenas,* or flowers of Christmas Eve.

A yucca lily rose high against the little adobe house, a great cluster of creamy bells at the top of its tall stem. Large showy hibiscus flowers swayed on thin branches, and against the blue sky rose the ball-like flowers of an acacia tree. There was the spicy fragrance of carnations in the air.

On Saturday morning the MacLarens visited the market, which overflowed from the covered portion onto the sidewalks. Some of the native Indians had only a tiny heap of peanuts to sell, or some coarse sugar cakes, or a few faggots. But other dealers displayed serapes, made in Tlaxacala, or fine drawn work and needlework from neighboring villages. There were palm-leaf hats, chocolate beaters, canes, pottery, and tiles, among other things.

James Sawders

A STREET SCENE ON MARKET DAY

Donkeys brought in great baskets of tomatoes and gourds, bubble-shaped jars, and net sacks of charcoal. There were bunches of flowers, including wild flowers from the hills. The children saw bright vegetables, golden cheeses, and fowls. They saw also blankets, rebozos, skirts, and handkerchiefs, with sandals and boots, for sale. Peter bought a clay toy bank, but he dropped it before he left the market. It broke into pieces which were soon trampled in the dust.

The MacLarens left the cool, high city of San

Luis Potosí on an air-conditioned train bound for Mexico City.

South of San Luis Potosí, Uncle Lee leaned over the back of the seat in which Peter and Nancy sat, to point out a field of maguey.

Now as the train sped onward, Peter began to laugh. So did Nancy.

"No need to point out maguey to us now," Peter observed. "We'll probably never see so much maguey again."

Maguey grew along the railway tracks. All over the rolling land it grew in long, green rows. It spread out over the plains, seeming to rise and fall in great green waves. The plants were a rich bluish-green and, in appearance, much like huge artichokes.

"They don't look very juicy," Nancy observed. "I'd never guess, to look at them, that they furnished *pulque*, the best known Mexican drink."

Peons carrying long gourds and pigskin sacks were bending over some of the plants in nearby fields.

"What are they doing, Uncle Lee?" Nancy inquired. "I suppose they're getting pulque. But how?"

"We may as well go over the whole process," Uncle Lee answered. "You see, the maguey plant grows for about seven years before it blooms. Then it withers and from the root sprouts another plant. Just before the plant blooms, the workers cut out the base of the plant,

shaping it like a great bowl. Sap gathers rapidly
in this bowl, five or six quarts a day. The flow
lasts three or four months. The sap, which is a
milky fluid, is called *aguamiel*, or honey water.
It stays sweet about twelve hours. So long as it
is sweet it is a pleasant drink that cannot hurt
one."

When the train pulled into the station of Mariscala, and the venders began shouting, "Aguamiel!" Uncle Lee went out on the platform and
returned with a cupful of the much-lauded drink.
He poured a small amount into paper cups which
he took from the water cooler of the train. Peter
and Nancy each took a sip. Nancy said, "I think
I've had enough; thank you, Uncle Lee."

But Peter declared, "It isn't bad at all. It
tastes a lot like buttermilk."

"Those peons you saw in the field suck the sap
up into the gourds they carry," Uncle Lee explained. "Then they pour it into pigskin sacks.
They carry the sacks to the plantation from which
it is to be shipped. From there it is sent to the
market at once.

"If you two don't get enthusiastic about aguamiel," Uncle Lee remarked, "you won't be real
natives. Aguamiel is the national drink. But
this 'honey water' isn't such a mild drink when it
has soured. It becomes pulque then."

The train had passed through more mountainous country and was now nearing Querétaro.

"We're not much more than a hundred miles

Ewing Galloway
CARRYING SACKS OF PULQUE TO MARKET

from Mexico City," Uncle Lee said. "Would you
like to stop off here?"

Querétaro which occupied the site of an Otomi
Indian town founded about 1400, proved to be a
delightful mixture of ancient and modern life.
The MacLarens rode on the street railway, visited
the Bank of Querétaro, and gazed upon the
governor's palace of basalt. But the ancient land-
marks of the city were more appealing. There
were the famous Hercules cotton mills, the Santa
Rosa convent, the old Bull Ring, the Plaza Zenea,
and the old aqueduct built centuries ago by the

James Sawders

THE OLD SPANISH AQUEDUCT

Spaniards. It still brought water to Querétaro.

The people seemed most proud of their Civil College and the Iturbide Theater and derived great pleasure from showing them to visitors who came to their city.

Out from the city at some distance were the opal mines. They had been worked from the earliest times, and there were not many stones left. The blue stones with their hearts of fire seemed to Peter and Nancy somehow like the golden-skinned, black-eyed workers. There was an outer calmness but an inward desire for better things. Both Peter and Nancy hoped the opals would bring good fortune to the modern Mexicans.

THE OLDEST CAPITAL IN AMERICA

THE train zigzagged upward from Querétaro toward Mexico City. Fields of maguey and corn gave way to scrub oak. At Tula, the ancient capital of the Toltecs, Uncle Lee pointed out the great cut in the hills by which the valley of Anáhuac must be kept drained to prevent floods. There was the monotonous hum of the rails as the hours flew by.

At the rim of a great natural bowl, Peter and Nancy looked down at a sun-drenched crater in which lay a gleaming, beautiful city surrounded by a jeweled necklace of lakes. The long slopes of the mountain rose ten thousand feet above steeples and domes as though proudly proclaiming the wonderful city.

"Popocatepetl is the landmark of the valley," Uncle Lee volunteered, looking over Peter's and Nancy's shoulders. "The Mexicans call it Popo. In Aztec the name means 'smoky mountain.' Popo is about eighteen thousand feet high, the highest mountain in all Mexico except Orizaba in the state of Veracruz."

"Popo's a volcano," Peter exclaimed. "Has it ever erupted, Uncle Lee?"

"There have been ten eruptions since records began," Uncle Lee answered. "It is said that Cortez let men down into its crater on ropes to get

sulphur for gunpowder. The amount of sulphur
that nature has stored in that crater is probably
beyond our comprehension. The Mexicans will
tell you that they have already removed about
100,000,000 tons. That is enough sulphur to
make matches to supply the world."

"It doesn't look very warm," Nancy observed.

"Nor is it," Uncle Lee agreed. "Its caves often
supply ice for the towns down on the plains.
Do you see Ixtacihuatl?"

"That's the mountain linked to Popo," Nancy
cried. "Our history said that when Cortez led his
army down to attack the Mexicans he made his
way over the saddle that connects the two mountains."

The swift train carried its passengers down
into the sunlit city, and the MacLarens found
themselves, with tourists and citizens, in the
Colonia Station. They joined the throngs that
poured out into the streets.

"I can hardly wait to see the city." Nancy
caught up with Uncle Lee as he strode ahead.
"It's the oldest big city in the western hemisphere, isn't it?"

"No one knows how old," Uncle Lee told her.
"When the Spaniards came, it was already a
large prosperous city. Historians say it was
founded several centuries before the first settlement of North America."

The MacLarens got into a taxi, and Uncle Lee
said, *"Plaza de la Constitución!* .... I'm going to

James Sawders

THE RESIDENTIAL DISTRICT OF MEXICO CITY

show you the largest plaza in Mexico City. We'll go to our hotel later. But I want you to see a cross section of this great city first. Try to picture the city as Cortez saw it on that November day in 1519 when he looked upon a scene never before viewed by a white man."

As Uncle Lee talked, the scene became alive. The black-bearded Spaniard rode his white horse, the first horse ever seen by Aztecs, into the city, and his silver armor gleamed in the warm, clear sunlight. His bright, dark eyes glinted at sight of the palaces, the markets, and the laden

barges, heavy with produce of all kinds. Montezuma, the Aztec emperor, glittering with gold
and jewels, came out to meet him.

Here, where Cortez had expected only wilder-
ness or savage life at best, was the richest city
he had ever beheld. As the Spanish leader and
his men followed Montezuma down a paved
street lined with stone buildings, their hearts
beat high with excitement. Their adventurous
eyes made note of the busy canals and market
stalls. Ahead stood the great palace of Montezuma's father in which Cortez and his men
were invited to rest.

Facing that palace was the great sacrificial
teocalli, or temple. Here the newcomers first
saw the horrible idol, the god of war. The idol
had huge, terrible eyes, a girdle of snakes about
its body, and a sheaf of arrows in its hands.
Precious jewels had been set into the metal. To
this god the Aztecs, as the Spaniards learned,
sacrificed many innocent people every year.

Uncle Lee ordered the driver to go slowly.
The great plaza proved to be a beautiful, large
park with many walks. Across the plaza, near
the site of the ancient Aztec temple, rose an
impressive cathedral. The first Christian church
in Mexico, Uncle Lee said, had been erected upon
the debris of the pagan temple here in Mexico
City. The present cathedral was the work of
several generations.

The MacLarens got out of the taxi and strolled

through the plaza. Their luggage went on to the hotel.

"We're on historic ground," Uncle Lee declared. "In 1521 a bloody battle between Aztecs and Spaniards was fought here. This plaza has seen one political party after another come into power. In 1822 Iturbide proclaimed himself emperor in this plaza. In 1847 Winfield Scott, our American general, raised the Stars and Stripes here. Seventeen years later Maximilian saluted his subjects from one of the balconies overlooking this plaza. In 1867 General Porfirio Diaz was acclaimed here as a 'hero and patriot,' and later, from the same balcony, denounced as a traitor and murderer. Here was the focal point of all the revolutions from 1910 to 1923. This is a place where much tragic history has been made."

"It certainly doesn't look like a place of terror now," Nancy decided. "It looks peaceful and prosperous."

She glanced about at the many palaces, shops, markets, and the cathedral that faced the square. Uncle Lee pointed out ten thoroughfares that ran toward the great plaza, and he named three of the most famous avenues, *Cinco de Mayo*, *Madero*, and the *16 de Septiembre*.

Peter was amazed by the amount of traffic. Tramcars clanged, motorcars whirled by, and numberless pedestrians strolled along, while overhead an airplane motor droned. There seemed to be almost as many foreigners as natives.

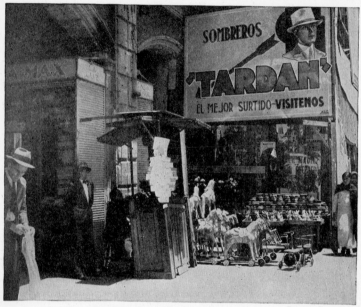

James Sawders

AN OPEN AIR TOY SHOP

"We'll walk along the west side," Uncle Lee decided. "I want you to see one of the oldest markets. It was first built in 1524 when city officials gave permission for dealers to build porticoes to shelter goods displayed on sidewalks. Until recently *evangelistas*, or letter writers, also plied their trade under these shelters."

Before arriving at the immense market the MacLarens saw sandals and shoes and sombreros for sale. These hats had been sent in from every region in Mexico.

"I thought sombreros were all more or less alike, especially in size and shape." Peter was puzzled. "Look at this lot, Uncle Lee. They're short and shallow. I never saw such low crowns."

"They're from Jalisco and Michoacán," Uncle Lee explained.

Peter paused a little later at a stall in which a pile of tall, conical hats with deep brims that rolled up gracefully were displayed.

"From Morelos," Uncle Lee said briefly.

"And those?" Nancy pointed at some large, cool-looking sombreros of rice palm leaf.

"From Jaracuaro," said Uncle Lee promptly.

The walls of the old arcade under which the MacLarens strolled reminded Peter of the billboards at home; at least, so he said. The ancient walls were plastered with posters advertising bullfights or with notices of lotteries.

The crowds were slow and good-natured. People did not shove each other, and no one appeared to be in a hurry. Children stopped to enjoy the sight of cheap candies. Some prospective buyers fingered the picture postcards. Others tried on eyeglasses, then laughed gaily at the sight they presented. The young girls chose cheap, bright trinkets from the jewelry displays.

"Nothing seems to cost very much," Peter observed.

Uncle Lee told them that the Merced Market sold merchandise very reasonably and handled a great quantity of it. People in some of the out-

Ewing Galloway

CARRYING GOODS TO MARKET

lying villages walked miles in order to sell their products here. The finer shops, he explained, were on the fashionable avenues where anything from blown glass to intricate filigree jewelry could be bought.

The stalls of ready-to-wear clothes were a delight to Peter, who wanted to take a real Mexican suit home to show the neighbor boys. He chose tight trousers, a gay jacket with many buttons, and a bright, collarless shirt. Nancy looked at the display of rebozos, the shawl-like garments

James Sawders

ONE OF MEXICO CITY'S OLDEST MARKETS

such as she had seen the native women wearing. It was a delight to her to see a few close at hand. Most of them were dark blue or brown or black with an allover design in white. The more expensive ones were brilliant in color with an allover design in black. Uncle Lee pointed out some of the hand-knotted long fringes, lacelike in their beauty.

Peter had moved on to look at the serapes. There was one black-and-white one from Toluca that he decided would make a wonderful rug.

Nancy was intrigued by the *morrales*, or colorful bags. But when she saw the tablecloths and
the napkins with the borders of animal designs
that had been worked in long-stitch by the Otomi
Indians, she couldn't quite decide what she did
want to buy. Uncle Lee wisely suggested that
actual shopping could be left until another day.

Peter shouted to his sister that she simply
must see the baskets at once. He pointed out
reed baskets from Puebla, ivory-colored fiber
ones from Guanajuato, and baskets with bands
of black-stained reeds. A lovely basket of magenta and green had come in from Michoacán.
Best of all was a colorful basket from Toluca.
The Toluca basket was light, strong, firmly
woven, and the designs of little men and animals
were delightful. It was hard to come away from
the stalls. Peter made a final purchase of a
straw man riding a straw horse.

"Of course," said Nancy, "the little boy has to
have at least one toy to play with."

But when Nancy observed the cunning work-
manship of the toy, she decided to purchase one
for herself.

Uncle Lee led the way to the south side of the
plaza.

"This is the *Portal de las Flores*, or the old
flower market," he explained. "Once canals led
right up to the plaza, and Indians beached their
canoes here."

A radio blared near by; an airplane soared over-

head; automobiles hurried past. It was hard
for Peter and Nancy to picture the peaceful old
flower market and the Indian canoes.

"Near here," Uncle Lee declared soberly, "Diaz
and his men saw slaves for sale. One record tells
of the amazement of the Spaniards as they went
from stall to stall. There were dealers in gold
and silver and precious stones. There were dealers in thread and rope. There were dealers in
chocolate, vegetables, and herbs. Men sold deer
and rabbits and dogs. The Spaniards enjoyed
honey, cooked roots, and salt from the market.

"A very definite idea of the wild life round
about the city was gained by the Spaniards when
they saw the skins for sale. There were skins
of pumas, ocelots, otters, deer, badgers, and
mountain cats.

"The pottery even in those days," Uncle Lee
continued, "was colorful, beautiful, and practi-
cable. Lumber was for sale, and stone knives
were common."

But the Spaniards saw no greater sight than
the great market as Peter and Nancy saw it.

A taxi stopped at the curb. Seated beside
Uncle Lee, they began a barrage of questions.

"They say," observed Uncle Lee archly, "that
the hardest post in our foreign service is the post
of ambassador to Mexico."

"Why?" Peter and Nancy asked together.

"People ask so many questions here," Uncle
Lee answered dryly.

THE FLOATING GARDENS

PETER and Nancy had planned to visit Xochimilco, the Floating Gardens, ever since they arrived in Mexico City. As they drank their breakfast chocolate in the hotel dining room, they felt rather impatient with Uncle Lee. He was enjoying his papaya very leisurely, and he kept saying, "Give me papaya any day in place of the finest muskmelon."

"Uncle Lee," Peter asked, thinking of the Floating Gardens, "don't you think it strange that Mexico City, which you say is nearly a mile and a half above sea level, should be built on a swamp?"

"Surely, Peter," Nancy put in, "you know how Mexico City came to be built here. It wasn't a question of whether the ground was swampy or not. The Aztecs saw an eagle perched on a cactus and holding a rattlesnake in its claws. According to their prophecies, here was the place to build Ten . . . Ten . . . "

"Tenochtitlan," Uncle Lee supplied. "The early Aztecs surely had a problem. There were many more lakes and marshes than there are now, of course. To protect the city from floods, they built many dikes in Lake Texcoco. Texcoco, by the way, was a salt lake. I imagine the city once looked a great deal like Venice. There was a

waterway for canoes and barges that ran away
out to Lake Texcoco. The Spaniards, striving to
do away with many floods, used Indian labor
to build the great Tajo de Nochistongo trench to
drain the valley lakes. The Indian labor was
slave labor, and many men died before the great
project was completed. But still floods came."

"The city looks safe enough now," Peter observed.

"It's been safe only since 1900," Uncle Lee surprised Peter by saying. "Up to that time Mexico
City had been diked and drained like a seaside
city, yet it was located near a continental divide.
Engineers finally solved the problem. They built
the thirty-mile Canal del Desague. I want you
two youngsters to think of it as you think of the
Roosevelt Dam and the Panama Canal."

"We will," Nancy promised, and asked, "Ready
now to take us to the Floating Gardens?"

"Tell us more about the canal first," Peter
begged. "Some day I'm going to be an engineer."

"I thought it was an aviator yesterday," Nancy
teased.

"Thousands of men worked for years to dig
this great ditch," Uncle Lee explained. "They
had to carry its tunnel more than six miles under
the mountains. You can scarcely imagine the
tons of earth that had to be moved."

"I can imagine the men and the teams," Peter
said, "and the steam shovels! And now Mexico
City is perfectly safe," he decided.

Nancy, who had seemed not particularly interested, made a sudden observation.

"Some of the old buildings look rather tippy, if you ask me," she said. "And some look as though they were sinking into the old swamp."

"You're right, Nancy," Uncle Lee agreed. "Waste water is controlled by the engineers, but underground streams are still a worry. The land on which Mexico City is built is swampy, and many a heavy building is slowly sinking. Some day, let us hope, the problem of underground seepage may be solved. Anyway, the Floating Gardens are one of the beauty spots of this swampy land. The name Xochimilco means, in Aztec, 'where flowers grow.' You'll not be disappointed."

The drive out to the gardens was a great surprise to both Peter and Nancy. The road led through cactus-lined lanes and Indian villages with their plazas ablaze with flowers.

Xochimilco itself was somewhat of a disappointment. At first sight it presented the appearance of a picnic ground. Bands were playing. Boys and girls were shouting and laughing. Gay parties, in boats and on land, were eating picnic lunches quite as they did in the amusement parks back home. Indians from all the hill villages had gathered to market their pottery, textiles, straw hats, and other products.

"The gardens don't seem to be floating," Peter complained.

Ewing Galloway

STRAW HATS FOR SALE!

"So I notice." Uncle Lee's bright eyes twinkled. "Back in the Aztec days they actually did float. Now they seem to be living on their reputation. The original idea was unique, anyway."

"What made them stop floating?" Nancy inquired.

"And what made them float in the first place, since they aren't floating now?" Peter added.

"The Aztecs," Uncle Lee hastened to explain, "plaited sticks and vines, and on the resulting rafts they spread a thick layer of rich dirt. In this dirt they planted vegetables and flowers.

James Sawders

A FLOWER SELLER ON THE CANAL

Such a garden could be poled anywhere the gardener chose to take it. But as the years passed, poles which had been stuck down to anchor a garden often took root. Other roots helped to fasten the garden to a permanent place. Even now you can see that there are water lanes between the various gardens. We'll hire a boat and make a little excursion among the flowers."

It was a very simple matter to hire a *chalupa*, or flat-bottomed boat with a gay awning, colorful cushions, and fragrant floral decorations.

While the MacLarens lolled at their ease, a smiling Mexican boy stood up and poled the boat along, much after the manner of a gondolier in Venice.

When they were actually among the floating gardens, Peter and Nancy felt the charm of their ancient surroundings. The boat moved between great beds of lilies and roses. Poppies bloomed in scarlet profusion. Marigolds gleamed in the sunlight. Sometimes the shade of ahuehuete trees fell across the watery path. The fragrance of giant sweet peas mingled with the spiciness of nasturtiums.

The vegetable gardens were almost as colorful and attractive as the flower gardens, and Peter decided that the tall corn compared favorably with the corn of Iowa. String music came from one of the boats. Songs drifted out in rich tones.

On some of the boats there was a restaurant service. Picnickers who had not brought lunches with them could purchase *enchiladas*, chili con carne, tortillas, fried beans, and aguamiel. Peter and Nancy were content, for the time being, with some fruit the boatman offered them.

He was a most agreeable man. When he learned that his passengers were Americans, he pointed out the ancient Viga Canal which, he explained, ran from Xochimilco into the city. Along this water highway Indians hauled fruit, flowers, vegetables, and fowl to the city markets.

It was late afternoon before Peter and Nancy

James Sawders

A VEGETABLE GARDEN IN XOCHIMILCO

could be persuaded to leave the luxury of their flat-bottomed boat with its soft cushions. The taxi driver who had brought them along the fifteen-mile drive through the Indian villages lay under an ahuehuete tree, his sombrero over his face. He rose and stretched when Uncle Lee nudged him, and a smile lighted up his dark, friendly features.

"Grasshopper Hill!" Uncle Lee instructed him. Then to Peter and Nancy he explained that Grasshopper Hill, or the forest of Chapultepec as it is called by the Mexicans today, was one of the beauty spots of Mexico City."

"It can't be any more beautiful than Xochimilco," Nancy decided. "Grasshopper Hill doesn't sound particularly inviting."

"It may be interesting," Peter conceded. "It's where one of the presidential palaces stands, isn't it, Uncle Lee?"

"Buildings!" scoffed Nancy. "After seeing the big cathedral, any other building would disappoint a traveler."

The long, pleasant drive brought the MacLarens to a stately park with noble old trees surrounding an imposing castle. The trees were so immense that they made both Peter and Nancy pause in awe. Even before Uncle Lee told them, they realized that those trees were probably the only living things that had seen Montezuma in all his glory.

"Five, probably six hundred years old!" Uncle Lee said as Peter and Nancy got out of the taxi and went to sit on one of the gnarled roots.

"What kind of trees are they?" Nancy asked, gazing about at the noble sentinels of Chapulin. "They look like a kind of evergreen."

"They are giant cypresses," Uncle Lee answered. "You saw some of the smaller specimens in the Floating Gardens."

Peter and Nancy now observed that the giant trees surrounded the hill on which stood the Castle of Chapultepec. It was there, Uncle Lee said,

James Sawders

CHAPULTEPEC CASTLE

that Montezuma had a summer palace. The present building, standing high on the hill as though to catch the sunlight, had, he said, a tragic history.

"Who built it?" Peter inquired. "I hope it stands forever."

"It was started in 1783 by the Viceroy Gálvez," Uncle Lee answered. "He did not finish it. In 1842 it was used as a military academy, and in 1847 its forty students helped to defend it against the Americans in the battle of Chapultepec. The lovely Empress Carlotta and the Emperor Maximilian occupied the castle in 1866. It was then the empress beautified the grounds and terraces, and rebuilt it along palatial lines. President Diaz

Paul's Photos

THE FOUNTAIN OF DON QUIXOTE

restored it and lived in it for many years. It
still is a presidential retreat. Many a troubled
ruler has looked down from its lofty towers on
the city with its guardian mountains."

"President Cardenas does not use it, though,"
said Nancy. "Remember, Peter, when we read
about that?"

"Yes," answered Peter, "and it also stated that
his is the only train in Mexico that does not carry
a guard."

As they walked on, Uncle Lee told them that
President Cardenas spends much of his time, not
in Mexico City, but in the country. There are
found Mexico's biggest problems.

Uncle Lee explained that President Cardenas
was responsible for giving the peons land of their
own and making them free. The Indians tell
him at great length about their needs, their
hopes, and their troubles.

Uncle Lee seemed to be leading the way
through the woods without any attention to direction, but suddenly Peter exclaimed, "Look!
There's the Quixote Fountain! Come, Nancy!"

He seized his sister's hand and ran with her
to the lovely fountain with its famous pedestals.

"Peter! You'd never believe it unless you saw
it!" Nancy was thrilled. "There are bookcases
in the pedestals, shelves with real books in them."

"Sure enough!" Peter exulted. "Plato and
Homer and Goethe and other famous writers!
What a grand place to read!"

Peter discovered many old people and young people, too, reading quietly in the woods all about the place.

"I'd like to sit on this bench near the fountain and read Cervantes' *Don Quixote*—in English, of course. I can't read Spanish," Peter said wistfully.

"The next best thing will be to carry a mind picture home," Nancy decided. "Peter, let's read *Don Quixote* together next summer, and let's pretend we're reading it on Grasshopper Hill."

"All right," Peter agreed. "Only it will be very hard imagining trees as big as these."

THE INDIAN FESTIVAL

PETER and Nancy had become quite used to Mexico City routine. They knew that the stores were open from eight to one and from three to seven. During the two hours of "nooning" every one went home to lunch and to enjoy a *siesta*, or afternoon nap. Then the town was almost dead. Later, traffic would come to life again; and since the traffic rules were neither strict nor well defined, it was necessary for pedestrians to scramble across the streets as best they could.

At first the stores confused the MacLarens. The names were never indicative of what the stores sold, nor did they indicate the ownership. "The Eden of the Poor Man" might give a pleasant mind picture, but it was not informative. Peter and Nancy had to look in the windows or peek into the stores to learn what was being offered for sale. If Uncle Lee wished to know the name of the dealer, he had to ask a clerk. The clerks invariably smoked the strong native cigarettes or cigars. In fact, nearly everybody except some of the women shoppers smoked in the stores.

The street names were quite as unusual as the store names. They were chosen to honor some special holiday or some hero or a saint.

Peter and Nancy became familiar with the

Ewing Galloway

AN AZTEC IN ANCIENT COSTUME

flat, three-cornered faces, typical of Indians of pure Aztec blood. They learned to recognize the Spanish aristocracy, too, for the aristocrats often had brown hair, blue eyes, and delicate features.

James Sawders

THE CARVED WALLS OF THE SECOND OLDEST
BUILDING IN THE NEW WORLD

The typical Mexican, a mixture of Aztec and
Spanish, had black, straight hair, dark eyes, and
warm brown skin.

One morning Uncle Lee took Peter and Nancy
out to Valbuena Field to meet friends who were
coming in on a passenger plane from El Paso.
Except for the Spanish spoken, the field was like
an American field. It was modern in every way.

Peter and Nancy were always conscious that
they were in a country much more ancient than
their own. Here in Mexico City America's first

sheet music and first book were published. Here the first money was coined. Here the first newspaper was printed in 1693. Appropriately it was called the "Flying Mercury." On this ancient ground Cortez built the first sugar mill and introduced domestic animals and farming methods to the Aztecs.

Out of the passenger plane from El Paso stepped Uncle Lee's best friends, Doctor Caine and his wife. From the Caines, Peter and Nancy were to learn much about the University. Already Uncle Lee was talking about art and literature and political problems with his friends. It seemed that the doctor had come to Mexico City to do some research work. From what he said, Peter and Nancy learned that the University classes were held in gorgeous palaces, in convents, and in museums.

The children were told that the University was founded in 1551 as "The Royal and Pontifical University of Mexico." By 1775 it had already awarded about a thousand doctors' degrees and about twenty-six thousand bachelors' degrees. It was closed near the middle of the nineteenth century, but reopened sixty years later as the National University of Mexico.

When Peter informed Doctor Caine that he thought he would work his way through the University of Mexico, Doctor Caine chuckled. That sort of thing just wasn't done. Although not an expensive university, Mexico had traditions to preserve. It was presumed that most of the students were aristocrats. The summer sessions, which many students from the United States attended, were important in more ways than one. Students learned their Spanish accurately, Doctor Caine maintained. They learned also to appreciate Mexico's problems. But most important of all, contact with Mexican students cemented a fine understanding and an affectionate regard between Mexican and American.

Doctor Caine said that he planned to spend the afternoon visiting a Mexican friend who lived a few miles out of the city. He invited Peter and Nancy to ride along, and they were delighted to accept his invitation. Doctor Caine's friend had three small boys who were playing in the yard with their pet burro when the visitors arrived. Peter and Nancy had such a good time that the afternoon passed quickly, and it was soon time to return to Mexico City.

"Come to Minnesota and visit our home some time. We'll let you play with our pony," called Peter as they waved good-by to the three boys and rode away.

The next day Doctor Caine escorted Peter and Nancy through the Dominican Monastery and the convent of Churubusco to impress them with the beauty and age of their chapels. He spoke of the ruins of deserted cities whose inhabitants had lived before the Aztecs. He took them to the National Museum to see the Calendar Stone,

James Sawders

THE THREE BOYS WITH THEIR PET BURRO

or Stone of the Sun, which had been part of the great Aztec temple. He pointed out the strange astronomical and chronological signs carved in the great stone. Peter and Nancy tried to look wise as Doctor Caine explained just how the Aztecs used the Calendar Stone as a sun dial and calendar.

They saw many images of Aztec gods, and great stones on which human beings were sacrificed to those gods. One of the best known was one in the shape of a reclining tiger.

That evening in the hotel Uncle Lee said, "I

Hugo Bremhe

IN THE NATIONAL MUSEUM

think Doctor Caine has taken great pains with you two youngsters the last few days in showing you the city."

"It's been fun," Nancy cried. "I've loved it out of doors. But it's always so cool in the evenings. Don't you think it's rather chilly in our rooms, Uncle Lee?"

"They don't seem to believe much in furnaces," Peter remarked. "All the buildings are cold."

Then Uncle Lee made an announcement that set his charges to shouting with excitement. The

Caines had taken a house, and the MacLarens were invited to be their house guests.

"We'll see a real Mexican house!" Nancy exulted. "Oh, Peter, we'll see how Mexican houses look on the inside."

The house to which the MacLarens drove was two stories high and made of colored tile instead of the usual adobe brick. A smiling man servant came to admit the MacLarens.

"He is called a *mozo*, or man of all work," Uncle Lee told Nancy. "He opens the door. He guards the house. Also, he acts as janitor. Servants are not such a luxury here as they are back home. Even a person of moderate means must have a mozo, a cook, and a laundress.

"Notice this big heavy door," he added. "Some of the old Spanish keys were so heavy that a man could not easily carry them with him. Probably that fact led to having servants sleep inside the door to let the family in.

"The servants live on the first floor," Uncle Lee explained as the mozo led them over the brick floor in the half-open walk around the patio.

The patio was like a garden space, with comfortable chairs and a bubbling fountain.

"The patio," Uncle Lee said, "is really a daytime living room. Notice how thick the walls of the house are, three or four feet, I'd say. Everything is very substantial. You'll find no wallpaper on the inside anywere, just paint or calcimine."

The mozo now led the way to the balcony that overlooked the flowery patio, and the MacLarens climbed the stairs. Off this balcony were the rooms in which the Caines lived. Mrs. Caine was there in a high-ceilinged living room to welcome her guests. She served tea while they waited for the doctor to return from the Thieves' Market.

Peter asked, "What can the doctor be doing in a place with a name like that?"

"He'll tell you about it when he returns," Mrs. Caine answered mysteriously.

"And probably he will take you there to visit tomorrow," Uncle Lee guessed.

The MacLarens found the high-ceilinged rooms delightful. On the brick floors were worn rugs, and in the middle of the living room was a small heater. The pipe ran out the window, for there were no chimneys.

"I was determined to be comfortable," Mrs. Caine confided. "Hence the stove! We certainly need it in the evenings."

After tea she led Peter and Nancy up to the roof. There were quite as many flowers on the roof as in the patio below. The chairs and cushions were colorful as well as comfortable.

"Moorish architecture," she explained. "The Moors of sunny Africa introduced this flat-roof style to Spain, and the Spaniards brought it to Mexico."

She explained that the thick roof was heat-proof, and that its flat brick-paved surface made it a most satisfactory place to sit in the evening, especially on warm summer nights. Laughingly Mrs. Caine pointed out the fact that the neighbors could come to see her by stepping from their roofs to hers.

"What happens when it rains?" Nancy asked practically.

"We take in the cushions and let the water drain off through the tiles that project beyond the walls," Mrs. Caine answered. "Of course, if you are a pedestrian you have to be careful. Passing my house, you might get a good drenching."

Nancy was permitted to peek into the kitchen where a Mexican woman was busy preparing a meal over an old-fashioned stove with charcoal burners. The kitchen was dark and inconvenient, but the cook seemed satisfied.

Doctor Caine had come home and was talking to Uncle Lee in the living room.

"They say," Doctor Caine said distinctly, "that whenever you miss anything, if you will go to an out-of-the-way open market and look for it, you will find it. I missed part of my stovepipe, but I found it. At least it looks like the same pipe."

"I wish Nancy and I could see the Thieves' Market," Peter sighed.

No sooner was the hint given than the request became a reality. Doctor Caine and Uncle Lee took Peter and Nancy to what appeared to be a jumble of shed roofs, and there they found the

James Sawders

THE MEDICINE MAN AND HIS SNAKE

oddest assortment of wares. Most of it was junk.
It was so hot and stuffy and odorous under the
sheds that they were glad to get out into the
sunlit street.

Walking a few blocks, they came upon a crowd
of people gathered around a medicine man and
his snake. Peter insisted on watching them
awhile.

As a climax to the day's adventures Doctor
Caine stopped at the *Monte de Piedad,* an official
pawnshop.

It was founded, the children learned, by a Mexican muleteer who had grown rich from a silver mine. Once he had been very poor. In gratitude for his own good fortune he provided a place where needy persons could secure loans without paying much interest.

"This pawnshop works like a bank," Doctor Caine explained. "On pledged articles one may raise any amount. It may be a few pesos. It may be thousands of dollars. And one may patronize this pawnshop without loss of dignity."

Peter and Nancy were amazed to learn that the pawnshop was once a part of the Cortez Palace. It was of elegant colonial style with fine patios. After all Doctor Caine had told them, they were not surprised to see a shabby Indian with a blanket over his arm rubbing elbows with a man who was offering jewels as collateral.

The next morning the doctor announced that he and Mrs. Caine had decided to go with the MacLarens to see the Otomi Indians perform their age-old rite of flying from a pole at the Corpus Christi festival at Pahuatlan.

When they left the train at Honey, an Indian guide was waiting with horses. As Peter tried to adjust the long stirrups, Nancy remarked that they looked like huge wooden shoes.

After a short climb through dense pine forests the trail suddenly turned downward. Doctor Caine said the cornfields looked as though they were glued onto the almost perpendicular slopes; and the Indian villages certainly looked like huge nests among the trees.

"See those little gray huts! Their thatched roofs almost touch the ground!" Peter called out.

"And see those women pounding clothes on the flat rocks," Nancy added.

Many Indians with large packs supported on their backs by a woven palm-leaf band across their foreheads called out "*Adiós*," as the Mac-Laren party passed them on the steep grade.

Once they met a pack of muleteers lumbering along with freight from Pahuatlan. Mrs. Caine was beginning to wish that she had stayed in Mexico City when suddenly the orchards and red-tiled roofs of Pahuatlan appeared.

The hotel opened onto a patio. Drying skins of pigs, which the Indians used for carrying pulque, made it smell a bit sour. Some Indian children were dancing on the narrow cobbled streets to the tune of a radio.

Although the MacLaren party was up at daybreak the market was crowded with Indians. The women wore richly embroidered shoulder capes, in patterns typical of each village; their cotton skirts were drawn tightly around their hips but hung full in front; their black hair was braided and decorated with brightly colored beads.

On the small plaza a straight pole, almost seventy feet high, rose from a narrow hole which had been partially filled with offerings such as live fowls, chocolate, cigarettes, corn, fruit, and many other things.

Three Indians carrying long ropes and a log of wood hollowed out and smeared with grease on the inside, climbed the pole by means of a thick vine which had been wound about it.

Carefully they placed the hollowed stump on top of the pole, like a cap, but left it free to revolve. Below the cap the ropes were carefully wound round and round the pole. A frame made of six sticks was hung just below the cap; then the long ropes which the Indians had wound around the pole were thrown over the frame with the ends dangling in the air.

Soon the *voladores*, or flyers, gaily dressed to represent birds, entered the plaza. One of the six, the *Malinche*, or man dressed as a woman, had long skirts fluttering in the breeze. One by one they climbed to the top of the pole. They looked like tiny dolls in the air; then one stepped up onto the top of the hollowed stump and commenced to dance. The other five, stationed on points of the platform, played rattles, flutes, and a drum.

Faster and faster the dancer moved to the rhythm, although one misstep meant death. Each volador danced about ten minutes.

The Malinche made every one gasp with fear as he leaned down and enfolded each of the others with a large colored square of cloth held with both hands.

Acme

THE FLYING POLE DANCE

After all six had danced and were in their places on the frame, they tied the ends of the ropes around their ankles and with a wild cry jumped into space. Down they came, gathering speed as the rope around the pole unwound.

Round and round the pole they flew, as the music changed to a livelier rhythm.

On the crowded plaza below, throughout the dance, the Indians waited in silence. With a tumult of rejoicing they crowded about the voladores when the latter safely reached the ground.

Back in Mexico City, Doctor Caine told Peter and Nancy that few were privileged to see the old rite of the flying pole and he feared before many years had passed it would be a lost art.

Peter and Nancy were certainly finding Mexico an amazing place.

CLIMBING AN EASY MOUNTAIN

PETER stared longingly at the snowy peaks of Popocatepetl, the Smoky Mountain, and Ixtacihuatl, the Sleeping White Woman, from the Caine porch.

"We're climbing Popo tomorrow," he exulted.

"You mean we're starting tomorrow," Nancy amended. "Mrs. Caine says it's a good three days' work, even though Popo has the reputation of being an easy mountain to climb. We'll need the same equipment we used in climbing the Alps."

"Oh, it's much easier to climb than the Alps," Peter decided. "You can tell that by looking at it. The time's coming when we shall be able to make the trip in Uncle Lee's car."

Uncle Lee made an odd grimace.

"I should not be surprised," he agreed, "if some day the road should lead to the top. The mountain belongs to a Mexican general, and he has offered it for sale. If some American concession should buy it, you will see sulphur, ice, and amusements offered at popular prices. However, that would spoil the romance.

"According to an ancient story Popocatepetl was a god and Ixtacihuatl a maiden. The two fell in love. But Ixtacihuatl's father had offered his daughter in marriage to any brave who would conquer his enemies for him. Popocate-petl was about to return triumphant to claim the reward when his rivals sent back false news of his death. The princess then became the victim of a strange illness. Neither witch doctors nor priests were able to cure her. She languished and died. Popocatepetl's grief was so great that he constructed a great pyramid upon which he laid his beloved Ixtacihuatl, and next to it another, where he himself stands holding a funeral torch to illuminate her eternal sleep."

"Yes," said Nancy, "you can see her any day, if you have any imagination, Peter, lying there with her head on her arm as though she were sleeping."

"You have enough imagination for us both," Peter declared. "I wonder," he continued, "what those two mountains look like on the other side."

"They don't resemble a god and a maiden," Uncle Lee said dryly.

Next morning Uncle Lee drove his car to Amecameca as a starting point. It was a little town, and it lay at the base of a steep hill called the Sacro Monte. Peter and Nancy would have liked to climb the sacred mountain, too, following the trail of the old trees that were hung with Spanish moss. They knew they would find the fourteen Stations of the Cross. Uncle Lee said the legend of each station was beautifully written in quaint old Spanish on Puebla tiles.

"There is an old church up there, too," Uncle

James Sawders

THE PEAK OF IXTACIHUATL

Lee continued, "from which can be seen the finest view in the country of Smoking Mountain and the Sleeping White Woman. But here is our guide, who is also our mozo. His wife is going along to keep Nancy company and take care of her."

The two stolid Mexicans, laden with supplies, smiled at the children. Uncle Lee insisted on carrying part of the food supplies in his pack-sack.

"Can't we leave that shovel at home?" he

demanded, seeing how awkwardly the mozo was adjusting it over his back.

"Leave shovel? Maybe not get home," the mozo retorted.

Peter and Nancy carried their woolen socks, sweaters, and winter coats in packsacks fastened comfortably over their shoulders with straps so that their arms would be free to use their alpenstocks. Nor would the mozo start until the three MacLarens had been equipped with spikes strapped to their boots.

The start was easy, but soon the party reached a stretch of soft sand. At first Peter and Nancy laughed because it was fun to watch their boots sink in. Soon, however, the going became a real task, and the children were glad when, looking up, they saw a woodland ahead.

The woodland was delightful, the air fresh, and the sky blue. On the ground were pine cones a foot long. It was in this wood that they stopped to eat some sandwiches and drink some bottled orange juice. It was high noon, and they had been climbing since early morning.

They passed out of the wood and saw open land with a wheat field on the side of the mountain. "Ripe wheat so early!" Peter cried. "Back home blizzards are roaring over our wheat fields."

A pine forest through which they went began to thin. The sun was going down. The valleys below were almost black, but the snowy summits of the mountains glowed brightly.

"Make camp," the mozo decided.

He made a shelter of boughs and built a small fire. His wife began to pat some prepared tortilla dough into cakes and to heat some chili. Uncle Lee insisted that some of Mrs. Caine's good sandwiches be added to the meal.

Without being urged to do so, Peter and Nancy began to pull on their woolen socks and to add sweaters, coats, and caps to their hiking outfits. They ate with cold hands, glad for the warm food and the warm dishes.

"I thought there was a stone hut or something around here," Uncle Lee said.

"For tourists," the mozo acknowledged.

"Well, I'd rather be called a tourist than freeze to death," Uncle Lee declared. "Besides, I'm responsible for the health of my niece and my nephew."

Peter and Nancy faced Uncle Lee with quiet determination. They did want the experience of camping out on Mount Popo.

Almost they were to regret it. The fire, as night descended, seemed like such a meager little fire, and the wind that swept down from the snow fields was bitter cold. Nancy snuggled closer and closer to the mozo's wife who shared a thick wool serape with her.

After a hot breakfast the five adventurers continued their journey without taking off one layer of the extra clothing in which they had slept.

"Much more pleasant to carry it on us than in

a packsack," Peter decided, his teeth chattering.

It was good to climb again. The exercise sent warmth all through one's body. But it was not easy. Peter and Nancy had a hard time keeping their footing in the tall, slippery brown grass. They were breathing with difficulty when they finally came to a trough hollowed out of a tree. The trough was full of icy water from one of the many streams that flowed down the mountainside from the snow fields.

The cold wind was even more piercing now, and there was a constant mournful wail. No one talked at all. Putting one foot ahead of the other required all the energy that the climbers possessed. Up and up and up they trudged.

Now the trees were left behind, the friendly trees. Side by side Peter and Nancy plodded through the loose lava. Their feet sank in with each step, and wearily they drew them out, one after the other. Whenever they looked up at the gleaming mountaintop they took heart. It seemed so close.

Lava and ice particles began to whip down into their faces. The only shelter was a group of huge rocks ahead. It grew colder and colder. And then Uncle Lee shouted that there was a hut close by.

It was a very crude hut, high up on that bleak mountain side, but to the MacLarens it seemed most welcome. In the tiny room was a small charcoal stove on which to cook supper. There

were crude bunks with coarse worn blankets at
one side. There was a table. The wind howled
all about the shelter, but it couldn't get in. Here
was contentment and rest and peace.

"Well," asked Uncle Lee, "does the climb end
here?"

Brother and sister glanced at each other. Together they had shared many adventures. Nancy
shook her head at Peter.

"All we need," said Peter, "is some supper and
then some sleep. We'll finish the climb in the
morning."

The first field of lava over which the party
passed at dawn of the following day was soft.
The going was laborious, but it was not danger-
ous. Frozen lava farther up presented a different problem. It was slippery and hard.

Nancy's cheeks were fiery red, and she was
gasping for breath in the thin air.

"Peter," she begged, "let's go a little slower."

"I'll help you," Peter offered.

As he attempted to reach out for his sister, his
foot slipped. All of a sudden he was sliding down
the slope at a mad speed. The mozo, far below,
had stuck his pick into the frozen lava. Evidently
he was not unused to such happenings. He
reached out for Peter, caught him, and held
him until he could get a foothold.

Uncle Lee praised the presence of mind of
both geographers. Peter had not grabbed at
Nancy when he felt himself slipping. And Nancy,

James Sawders

THE LAST STRETCH OF THE CLIMB

although terribly frightened, had not looked
about and lost her own foothold.

The frozen lava gave way to snow fields.
Whenever Nancy's courage lagged, she raised
her eyes to the snow fields ahead. Surely, she
reasoned, snow would be much easier to walk on
than the frozen lava. It looked so soft and clean.

The mozo was organizing the party for the last
stretch of the climb. He was to lead the way,
Peter to follow him. The mozo's sturdy wife
took her place behind Peter. Nancy was sand-

wiched in between her and Uncle Lee, the safest place. Uncle Lee gave dark glasses to them all. Why all this preparation when the snow field was so close at hand?

Nancy soon discovered the cause of all the precautions. The wind had long since blown away any soft snow flakes that might have clung to the mountain side. The snow was not soft. It had formed a hard, slippery crust.

The shovel played a very important part in the ascent. With an ice pick the mozo cut away the surface hardness, and with his shovel he made a stairway in the snow so that the little party might climb up more easily. Clouds swirled below. One foot before the other, eyes constantly on the trail, the little party climbed.

At last the mozo gave a shout. Peter and Nancy, who thought it was only a rest signal, lay flat on their stomachs, exhausted and having difficulty with their breathing. There was a deep silence. In that deep silence Uncle Lee chuckled.

"Don't you want to see it?" he inquired.

Peter and Nancy sat bolt upright. They were resting on the edge of Popo's crater. They stared at walls of black obsidian, the hard flint from which the Aztecs made their knives and arrowheads. Far, far down were acres of yellow sulphur, and vapors rose from crevices and cracks in the crater's floor.

Dizzily they got to their feet and looked down

into the valley. There lay Mexico City, with its blue lakes, like a city in a fairy tale. Weariness dropped away. The never-to-be-forgotten picture was worth the climb.

Part of the going down was sheer, rowdy fun. The mozo and his wife unwrapped the straw mats they had been carrying. Peter sat down on one mat with the mozo, and down they slid on a path that showed signs of having been used. The mozo used his staff as a brake.

"That's the way sulphur is taken down," Uncle Lee explained to Nancy.

He, Nancy, and the mozo's wife seated themselves on the second mat. Both Uncle Lee and the Mexican woman used their staves as brakes. Dodging rocks and crevices, they slid farther in two minutes than they had climbed in an hour.

It was good to be back to the forest line again, to the friendly trees.

When at last the little party sat before a hot supper in the comfortable hotel in Amecameca, every one sighed in happy contentment.

Suddenly Nancy giggled.

"Remember, Peter," she asked, "what a hard time we had in the sixth grade learning to pronounce Popocatepetl?"

"But a worse time to spell it," Peter agreed. "It was almost as hard to spell it then as it is to climb it now. Whoever said Popo was an easy mountain to climb?"

"You did, for one," Nancy reminded him.

A PILGRIMAGE

PETER and Nancy, back in Mexico City, being treated for wind burn and sore muscles, were quite content to view Popocatepetl and Ixtacihuatl from the Caine roof. It was pleasant to review their experiences before so appreciative an audience as the Caines. They had not realized how many churches there were in the Anáhuac Valley until they looked down upon the city from the top of Popo. Actually the capital had seemed to be built of towers and domes.

"One thing, we've seen the most famous church in Mexico," Peter remarked, "the great cathedral in the Zócalo."

"It's the biggest, the most impressive, and perhaps the most historic," Doctor Caine conceded, "but it isn't the most famous. Surely you've heard of Guadalupe."

"Yes, we have," Nancy answered. "Uncle Lee says we're to see it if we have time."

"Well, you'd better take time," Doctor Caine advised. "You'll hear it said a good many times, and it's true, that Guadalupe is to the Mexicans what Benares is to the Hindus, Mecca to the Mohammedans, and Jerusalem to the Jews and Christians."

"I wish that you had been here on the twelfth of December," Mrs. Caine put in. "That is the

Ewing Galloway

MAKING TORTILLAS

national religious holiday in Mexico. The faithful flock to the sanctuary of Guadalupe by the thousand, rich and poor alike. You should see them. They come from all over Mexico, bringing their babies, their blankets, and their cooking utensils. They prepare their chili stews and tamales over charcoal fires, squatting in alleys and streets. They patronize the refreshment stands where tortillas and other Mexican foods are served. They laugh, talk, visit, and attend mass as they celebrate in the highest of spirits."

Mrs. Caine then went on to tell of the venders,

who invariably lined the roads, selling everything
from cheap jewelry to red lemonade, bananas,
sugar cane, pineapples, and rosaries. The rosaries were usually of glass or carved wood, she
said, but they might be of silver, or even of the
fretted gold work that comes from Yucatán.

"The strangest things are the 'deer-eyes,' "
she continued, "to be hung about the neck as a
protection against the evil eye, oranges wigged
with red corn floss as an offering to the local
Indian goddess, and the carved serpent canes,
once used in pagan ceremonies. The Mexican,
along with his modern Christianity, still retains
much of his ancient Aztec belief."

Uncle Lee, who had been busy in the living
room getting off his mail, now appeared on the
roof.

"When are we going to Guadalupe, Uncle
Lee?" Nancy inquired. "I think we should make
it a pilgrimage, don't you?"

"Yes, indeed," Uncle Lee agreed. "It's only
three miles or so. We'll start tomorrow morning after breakfast and walk."

"It will be lovely to walk," Nancy agreed
somewhat weakly, and Peter said, "Good idea,"
without much enthusiasm.

"Stop teasing them," Mrs. Caine commanded.
"I notice you didn't take a walk yourself this
morning in this rarified air."

The next day Uncle Lee brought his car to the
door early. As it purred slowly out of the town

along a road flanked by black and white poplars, he asked, "Do you want to hear the story of how the famous church came to be built? It's on the hill of Tepeyac, and Juan Diego is the hero."

It was most appropriate to hear the story as the car passed slowly by the fourteen chapels along the route, for each chapel represented one station of the Cross.

Straight ahead loomed the pink cathedral that had been built in 1792. Above the cathedral, on the high-walled hill, stood a worn, white chapel, its towers rising against the turquoise-blue sky. The hill had been terraced with the tombs of the Tepeyac cemetery.

High above the white chapel on the hill stood three crosses.

"The chapel is said by critics to be a perfect gem of Mexican Mudejar architecture," said Uncle Lee. "Above the entrance are yellow and azure tiles of the most enchanting beauty. The deep windows are star-shaped. Inside there is a ceiling beautifully decorated with cherubim. The altars are green—but here we are."

Uncle Lee parked the car behind a refreshment stand. He led the way up the hill through a lane of green and pink houses. Together the MacLarens joined the pilgrims, climbing the stairway cut in solid rock in order to reach the church. One very old woman climbed on her knees; whether out of piety or because of an infirmity, the MacLarens could not tell.

James Sawders

THE FLOWER MARKET AT GUADALUPE

"A stone carving of sails and the mast of a vessel used to stand here as a memorial," Uncle Lee told Peter and Nancy. "It was over two centuries old and had been erected as a thank offering by sailors who, having prayed to the Virgin of Guadalupe in a storm, were saved. You'll see a good many thank offerings but none more dignified nor more impressive than the stone sails were before an earthquake destroyed them."

The MacLarens looked down on the village. All the roofs were flat and many of them cracked and eroded. Uncle Lee said that cacti and chayote vines ate into such walls. The towers of the cathedral below rose in dignity against green trees. The streets rayed out from the cathedral and then seemed to lead away in all directions.

Most of the pilgrims ascending the stairs were native Mexicans, for the men invariably wore sombreros and the women wore rebozos. Some stopped to buy flowers at the street stands.

"There are plenty of thank offerings in here," Uncle Lee observed as they entered the chapel.

Many pictures lined the walls, pictures of persons being dragged from under trains or automobiles, persons undergoing surgical operations, and others escaping from wild beasts.

The life-size image of the Virgin glittered with jewels and precious stones. They seemed to make an aura for her.

The waters of the magical spring drew every pilgrim. Uncle Lee told Nancy that it was said if any stranger drinks the water, he would be sure to return to Mexico.

Peter and Nancy had expected a cold spring of purest water. They were very much disappointed to find it brackish water that boiled and bubbled. It had a very unpleasant odor. The copper dippers that were chained to a rail were being used by all the pilgrims, sick and well alike. Many were filling bottles with the sacred water to take it home with them. The stones were slippery from the water that had been spilled.

THE MYSTERIOUS PAST

THE MacLarens were consulting Doctor and Mrs. Caine in the Mexico City house.

" 'The Place of Those Who Have the Gods' lies just thirty miles to the northeast," Doctor Caine informed Uncle Lee. "San Juan Teotihuacan is worth going to see, and you will find no better motor highway out of Mexico City."

"Is it an Aztec ruin?" Peter inquired.

"No, it belongs to an earlier civilization than the Aztec; that of the Toltecs." Doctor Caine squinted through his thick lenses at Peter. "The Toltecs were forerunners of the Aztecs. You will have a great time climbing the pyramids."

"Pyramids! Sounds like Egypt," Nancy volunteered. "Maybe we'll see mummies!"

"The Toltec pyramids were not designed for places of burial, Nancy," Mrs. Caine corrected her young guest. "They were really temples. The two at San Juan Teotihuacan were dedicated to the worship of the sun and the moon."

The drive out to Teotihuacan with Uncle Lee the following morning was exciting to Peter and Nancy, armed as they were with information furnished by the Caines.

As the car sped over the road, Peter observed that the Mexican mode of travel was much slower than that of the American tourists.

Ewing Galloway

THE WOMEN WALK WHILE THE MEN RIDE

"And it seems to be customary for the women to walk while the men ride the burros," commented Nancy, as they passed a family traveling in that fashion.

The gay chatter ceased, however, when two great hills loomed up on the plain ahead. The plain was almost devoid of vegetation. Near by, said Uncle Lee, were quarries that had been worked since early days.

The larger of the two great man-made piles proved to be the Pyramid of the Sun. It did not seem as big to Peter and Nancy as the Cheops

James Sawders

THE PYRAMID OF THE SUN

in Egypt, but Uncle Lee declared that it was quite as large though the proportions were different.

Getting out of the car, the MacLarens examined the imposing hill. They saw that it was built in five sections, or terraces. Doctor Caine had said that it was 216 feet high and 750 feet wide at the base.

"Once," Uncle Lee explained, "there was a temple on the summit and inside it a great statue of the sun god. It had been carved from a single block of porphyry."

The steps leading up between the cemented terraces were badly eroded, but it was still possible to make the ascent quite comfortably. While the MacLarens were climbing, other tourists appeared. Several of the women carried sun umbrellas, and Nancy began to wish she had brought hers, too.

From the top of the pyramid the party viewed other pyramids and mounds below. They saw that an ancient paved road led from the base of the Pyramid of the Sun between mounds to another pyramid about a half mile away.

"The Pyramid of the Moon," Uncle Lee announced. "And that road is known as the 'Highway of the Dead,' because the mounds that flank it are burial mounds."

The road continued from the Pyramid of the Sun to the citadel which must once have been the center of the now ruined city.

Near the citadel the MacLarens saw a pyramid temple of Quetzalcoatl, with its plumed serpent decorations, and another temple of Tlaloc, god of rain. There were other small pyramids and altars, altars upon which fine young men and lovely young girls had been sacrificed to these gods of destruction.

The morning was scarcely gone when the MacLarens returned from San Juan Teotihuacan.

After lunch Uncle Lee followed a road to the southwest, climbing out of the valley into the Toluca Mountains. Ten miles from Mexico City

the road branched off, and soon a little town
appeared set in groves of great trees.

"*Desierto de los Leones!*" Uncle Lee announced.
"In plain English, 'Desert of the Lions.' "

"Where are the lions?" Peter inquired.

"And where is the desert?" Nancy asked.

"The name is certainly a misnomer, isn't it?"
Uncle Lee chuckled. "There isn't a desert here,
and probably no lion. But the Carmelite monks
who came here in the seventeenth century chose
the name. It reminded them of the dangers
suffered by their brother workers in Africa."

Leaving the city of lovely parks and drives,
Uncle Lee followed the road onto the highway
again.

"It's only thirty-five miles to Toluca," he said.
"We really should see the capital of the state of
Mexico."

"I thought Mexico City was," Peter began,
then caught himself. "I know better. The form
of their government is much like ours. The *Estados Unidos Mexicanos* means 'The United States
of Mexico.' Long ago, Uncle Lee, you told us that
there were twenty-eight states in Mexico, two
territories, and a federal district. Of course, the
capital is in the federal district, and it is also in
the state of Mexico."

"It seems funny," Nancy put in, "that the name
Mexico should be given to a city, a state, and a
country. Still, New York's much like that. It's
a city, a county, and a state."

James Sawders

PREPARING FIBER FROM THE MAGUEY PLANT

Uncle Lee stopped the car so the children could see an old woman who was working with a huge pile of fibers.

"I suppose you will be surprised to know that

Ewing Galloway

A MEXICAN HACIENDA AND A FIELD OF MAGUEY

this fiber comes from the maguey plant. Most tourists think only of aguamiel or pulque when they think of the maguey plant. But the fibers of the plant are a very important raw material, used in making rope and many of the baskets you see in the Mexican markets."

"I think that most of the fiber baskets look much better than the aguamiel tastes," remarked Nancy as they climbed back into the car.

Uncle Lee had remarked, as the car purred along the good road, that Toluca was more than

8,700 feet above the sea and nine hundred feet above Mexico City. Naturally Peter and Nancy had expected to see a mountainous little city and were amazed to find it located on a wide plain, a plain beautifully cultivated. The mountains were in the background with snowy summits rising against azure blue sky. Spread out on the plains were many *haciendas*, or ranches, the main houses often as large and impressive as fortresses.

In the town itself were several plazas, bright with flowers, and the picturesque El Carmen church. But it was the market which drew the attention of the MacLarens, one of the best in Mexico, Uncle Lee declared, at which to buy blankets, pottery, toys, embroideries, and baskets.

A guide offered to take them to a volcano called Nevado de Toluca. In the crater, he said, were two beautiful lakes.

"From the summit you may see Popo," he promised. "And on a very clear day you may even catch a glimpse of the Pacific Ocean."

"Not today," Uncle Lee decided. "We are meeting the Caines for dinner at Sanborn's, located in the House of Tile. It is said to be the handsomest manorial house in Mexico."

"It certainly has been a day of buildings," Nancy observed in the car on the way back. "Pyramids, monasteries, old churches, and now . . . "

"An old restaurant," Peter supplied. "But it has the best food in Mexico, I've heard. Let's hurry!"

THE LAND OF CORN

THE train sped eastward in a wide curve of tracks. For some time Uncle Lee had been telling Peter and Nancy about Tlaxcala, one of the smallest of the twenty-eight states. It was the Tlascalans who had helped Cortez in his conquest of Mexico, for the Tlascalan tribe had long been at enmity with the Aztecs. In return for their services to the Spanish Crown these tribesmen had been left in control of their lands. Even today, Uncle Lee maintained, there is still an air of independence about the Tlascalans, not usually found among a poor people.

"I thought Tlaxcala was the 'Land of Corn,' " Nancy said, as the train hummed onward. "That seems to imply plenty of everything."

"I'll let you judge for yourself," Uncle Lee decided.

The MacLarens got out at a station where a number of station wagons drawn by mules were waiting for the passengers. Peter was amazed that Tlaxcala, the capital of the state of Tlaxcala, should be several miles from a railway.

Near its outskirts the town ran into a dry, rolling plain. It looked level enough, but Uncle Lee said it was bumpy. Beyond was some farm land. Here was corn at last.

"It seems funny to see it cut and piled in

heaps instead of being set up in shocks," Peter observed.

A farmer was plowing one field, getting it ready to plant, for the spring comes, as Uncle Lee had said, very early on the Mexican plateau.

"I suppose the paper dolls will soon be at work." said Nancy.

Mrs. Caine had told them the Indians believed that air, fire, earth, rain, and mountains were represented by spirits which must be pacified. In the spring dolls, with hands raised in prayer, were made from tissue paper and colored the same as the plants they were to represent. After the village *brujo*, or priest, chanted over the dolls, the natives cherished them and took them out to the fields as offerings to the spirits.

There seemed to be a great deal of maguey, more maguey than corn, in fact. Both the corn and the maguey were very dusty.

The town itself, with its three thousand inhabitants, was a lovely, quiet place. On a terraced hill near the main plaza was the Church of San Francisco.

"That church," Uncle Lee announced, "is the oldest church in North America."

The hotel was shabby, and the MacLarens had to ask for water, soap, and towels. The black-eyed Indian girl shook her head over the queer request. But the patio was so lovely that Nancy forgot her bleak room. There was the spiciness of carnations in the air, the brilliance of geraniums, and the richness of bougainvillea climbing the old walls.

While they lunched on Mexican food in the dark little dining room, the MacLarens patronized a vender of flowers who came to their table. Evidently that was a mistake. Other venders swarmed about the table offering peanuts, vegetables, fruits, and even shoeshines. The proprietor finally shooed them away.

In the afternoon the MacLarens visited the Church of San Francisco. Uncle Lee pointed out the great stone font where the four Tlascalan chiefs had been baptized in the days of Cortez. The pulpit, Peter and Nancy learned, was said to be the place where the Christian gospel was first preached on the American continent.

The next morning the MacLarens visited the market as a matter of course. It was a lively market that handled everything from turkeys to red and white radishes a foot long. Although the country looked very dry, the market fairly bulged with potatoes, tomatoes, garlic, peppers, peanuts, and popcorn, as well as livestock. Corn was only one of the many products. Nancy was particularly interested in the serapes one man had for sale.

Peter and Nancy were impressed by the surprising abundance, but, strangely enough, what they were to remember most clearly about Tlaxcala was the view, a magnificent view of the two mountains, Popocatepetl and Ixtacihuatl.

James Sawders

A SERAPE SELLER

Never had the snow seemed whiter, the sky bluer, or the sunshine more golden.

But back on the train the following morning, their thoughts flew onward. Uncle Lee had announced, "We are to visit the 'City of the Angels' next," and, to be more explicit, had added, "Puebla."

Nancy wanted to know why Puebla should be called the City of the Angels and learned that Puebla was founded in 1532. It had not existed when the Spaniards came. According to legend, angels appeared to a priest in a dream telling him just how to lay out a city in that particular location.

Like Tlaxcala the city was guarded by the two volcanic mountains, Popo and The White Woman. But from Puebla another mountain could also be seen. To the west rose Orizaba, the highest peak in all Mexico.

At first Peter and Nancy had an impression of little low houses and church domes, but after they had made themselves comfortable at a good hotel in Puebla, they set out to explore in earnest. Uncle Lee remained behind to attend to his mail.

Alone they discovered the real beauties of the town. It was the City of Tiles, and the MacLaren children soon realized that in addition to manufacturing soap, paper, glass, flour, and pottery, Puebla really was most proud of its tiles and its onyx. Many of the domes of the churches glittered with bright colored tiles.

Peter and Nancy strolled along street after street to look at the old houses whose fronts were covered with tiles formed into mosaics of birds, animals, and even saints. Some houses were a creamy white, but the great majority were tinted in gay colors. Although the sun shone, the air was cool and it was a delight to walk briskly. At last they followed a crowd of worshipers into a great cathedral.

"It's like a gold cathedral!" whispered Nancy. She glanced up and around.

James Sawders

THE CATHEDRAL AT PUEBLA

It was one of the richest and handsomest churches the children had seen. Peter stopped before the splendid altar made entirely of colored Puebla onyx while Nancy gazed and gazed at the many beautiful old paintings. Much of the interior was actually incrusted with gold and that vision of the golden interior remained with the children long after their visit to Puebla.

Toward noon they hurried to meet Uncle Lee in the principal plaza near a fountain that he had designated. Here the colored tiles had been used in making the fountain base. Uncle Lee was watching the colorful parade of gaily dressed people who strolled through the flower garden and under the tall trees.

"Puebla, in spite of the legend," Uncle Lee said, "was really built by the Spaniards to protect the route to the sea. It has been the scene of much fighting. Wherever you go you'll find some tablet or statue commemorating an event in Puebla's historic past.

"I have rented a car," he added, rising. "I thought we'd have lunch, and then drive out to Cholula."

"Another shrine?" Nancy inquired.

"Yes," Uncle Lee answered. "But it is not an ordinary shrine. You'll find it amazing."

After lunch Uncle Lee stopped in a shop to see a display of fine onyx table tops, fireplace panels, and interior designs.

Then the three were in the car again and Uncle Lee was saying, "Long before the Spaniards came to Mexico, Cholula was an important city. It contained the principal shrine of Quetzalcoatl, the chief Toltec and Aztec divinity. Pilgrims came from far and near to worship in the great temple. Puebla was then undreamed of."

"And today?" Peter urged.

"Today," said Uncle Lee, "Puebla, as you know, is a prosperous city of 100,000 people. Cholula is just a small town to which curious tourists flock."

"We are a good sample of the curious tourists,"

Nancy laughed. "Why go to Cholula at all, then, if it's just a small town?"

"A famous pyramid is there. I heard the Caines talking about it," Peter announced. "That won't be much of a surprise for me."

The short drive came to an end. Uncle Lee cried, "There it is, the great teocalli or pyramid."

Nancy breathed a deep sigh of ecstasy.

"Uncle Lee!" she exulted, "it's the most amazing thing we've ever seen in a pyramid. That wonderful church with its gleaming, tiled dome at the top of that huge pile of earth is inspiring."

Peter had not spoken. He had heard the Caines tell about the proportions of this greatest of pyramids in Mexico. He knew that the mound measured one thousand feet on a side, that it covered an area of forty-two acres, and that it rose two hundred feet in the air; but mere figures had not prepared him for the sight of a church with gleaming dome standing at the top of a grass-grown hill as if overlooking the land below.

In ancient days the temple had stood there with its statue of Quetzalcoatl. A gold collar and a jeweled scepter had bespoken his power, while men, women, and children climbed the steps to worship or to be sacrificed. Now a Christian church, with its teaching of tolerance and love, replaced ancient symbols of hate and cruelty.

"Cholula," said Peter quietly, "was once considered a sacred city. Now it is one truly."

CALLING ON CAPITAL NEIGHBORS

"WE can't stay in Mexico City much longer," Uncle Lee decided as he led the way to his car in front of the Caine house. "Our excursions will have to end in a few days."

Peter and Nancy were sober as Uncle Lee drove toward Cuernavaca on a perfect, sunny winter morning. But as he began to tell them about the town they were to visit, smiles lighted their faces. Cuernavaca, he said, was three thousand feet lower than Mexico City and was already famous as a health resort. It escaped the cold winds of the plateau and the weather was always mild.

As they entered the town, it seemed as though every lovely, tinted house was set in a garden of palms and covered with bougainvillea.

Uncle Lee took his fellow travelers first of all to the palace built by Cortez, where, on the walls of the loggia, they viewed the rich frescoes depicting the conquest of Mexico. The frescoes had been made by the famous Mexican painter, Diego Rivera, and they were a gift, the children learned, of Dwight Morrow, United States ambassador to Mexico. He had loved the quiet little town and had made the gift as an expression of his regard.

"And now," Uncle Lee announced, "we shall

lunch in the loveliest place we can ever hope to see, the Borda Garden Inn."

Uncle Lee's enthusiasm was mild compared to that of Peter and Nancy when they walked through an exquisite garden in which birds sang, flowers bloomed, and the sun shone on the waters of a swimming pool.

"This was the favorite retreat of the Emperor Maximilian and the Empress Carlotta," Uncle Lee said.

"It's the loveliest place we have seen in all Mexico," Nancy decided. "I feel as though I were in paradise."

"A mere human being designed it," Peter put in. "Doctor Caine said that he was a French mining engineer who made a fortune in Mexico."

After a delicious lunch eaten in one of the colonnaded corridors that overlooked a flower garden, the MacLarens lingered in the gardens. Finally they got back into their car, and Uncle Lee made the announcement, "Now we shall go to view a national monument."

"I refuse!" Nancy cried staunchly. "Another monument!"

"I join in the mutiny," Peter agreed. "After this inn at Cuernavaca not even a national monument will do."

Uncle Lee kept on driving. The road was good, and five, ten, twenty, and then thirty miles clicked off on the speedometer. The car ran into a narrow valley and on into a town so delightfully

Ewing Galloway

A PICTURE-BOOK TOWN

quaint that Nancy said it looked like a picture-book town. The red-tiled roofs topped pretty little stucco houses that lined the crooked streets or perched on the edge of ravines, on high terraces, or near small bridges.

Peter and Nancy had already seen many beautiful and distinctive churches in Mexico, but they stared in open admiration at the church that seemed to dominate this little town. The great dome had been constructed of vivid tiles. The ornate towers were, by contrast, of a pink stone so delicate of shade that it reminded Nancy of apple blossoms. Yet there was nothing frail about the two towers as they rose against the soft blue of the sky. They were strong and lasting and beautiful.

Uncle Lee parked the car near the church, and the children gladly followed him into the dim, quiet, cool interior, which was quite as impressive as the exterior. Carved woods, decorations in gold, and splendid mural paintings bespoke fine taste.

"Who built it?" Peter asked when, at last, the three MacLarens came out of the subdued light into the brilliant sun.

"The same Frenchman that built the palace and the gardens at Cuernavaca," Uncle Lee answered. "He made his fortune in silver mines. Joseph le Borde! The church is an expression of his thanks to God for his good fortune."

"The church is no lovelier than the town or its setting," Nancy maintained as they passed an old fountain.

"Cortez lived near this town," Uncle Lee added. "His main object was to mine the silver. Many a rich vein lies in these hills."

"Now, aren't you glad we changed your mind about going to see a monument?" Nancy challenged her uncle.

"Even if it were a national monument?" Peter's glance teased Uncle Lee. "This is worth a thousand monuments. What's it called, Uncle Lee?"

"Taxco," Uncle Lee replied. "The town hap-

James Sawders

AN OLD FOUNTAIN IN TAXCO

pens to be the national monument I wanted you to see. The Mexican government has decided that no changes may be made or new buildings erected without special permission. The officials think that the whole town should be preserved as a — ''

"National monument," Nancy interrupted, unabashed. "Well, if there were more national monuments like Taxco, Peter and I wouldn't grumble about visiting them."

"Indeed, we wouldn't," Peter agreed.

"We can't leave Taxco without having a bite to eat at one of the street restaurants," remarked Uncle Lee.

Ewing Galloway

AN OUTDOOR RESTAURANT

Then he led the way to a place across the street where Mexican food was cooked and served out of doors.

The next morning when Uncle Lee announced that he was driving out to see a "gourd of blooming flowers," Peter and Nancy looked wise. The gourd of blooming flowers proved to be Uruapan, a little town on the western slope of the central plateau. Uncle Lee said the early Spaniards spoke of it as the "Paradise of Michoacán."

The whole countryside through which the MacLarens drove was tropical in its plant life. Bananas, oranges, and figs grew in the moist, warm soil. The coffee was reputed to be the best in all Mexico, and Mexicans were good judges of coffee.

Taxco was still fresh in the minds of Peter and Nancy, but they found this new town quite as delightful. For one thing, water in rivulets ran down the sides of the streets and in some parts of the town, even flowed down the middle of the cobbled streets. Each little tile-roofed house had its patio in which roses, magnolias, and poinsettias bloomed.

In the little shops, run by friendly tradesmen, were displays of Uruapan lacquer ware that had been made in the neighboring villages, the same lacquer ware that Peter and Nancy had seen displayed in the finest shops in Mexico City.

As another surprise Uncle Lee drove on a few miles instead of turning back on the road over which he had come.

Peter was just saying, "Isn't it funny, Nancy, that we always thought of Mexico as a land of desert and cactus?" when suddenly there came to his ears the thunder of water, and before them was a waterfall that plunged into a swirling pool below. Through tiny cracks leaped countless little falls. The cascades were fairylike in their beauty.

"The Falls of Zararacua," Uncle Lee announced. "And the stream is called the Rio Cupatitzio."

Uncle Lee left the car at the hotel and the MacLarens boarded a train, a branch of the

Mexican Central, to visit Mexico's great mining town, Guanajuato.

It was located in a narrow gorge, so steep that many of the streets turned into steps as they wound up the hills. Uncle Lee said that beneath the houses, ore dumps, and shaft housings were endless tunnels. The town had been built directly over the gold and silver mines. Guanajuato was formerly the richest mining city in Mexico. The Veta Madre, said to be the richest silver mine in the world, had been worked there. At one time no expense had been spared in building handsome promenades, gorgeous parks, and impressive buildings.

Of course, there were churches. The most elaborate one had been erected by Conde de Rul, owner of a silver mine. It was called the Church of San Cayetano, and it was so elaborate and gorgeous that it presented a rather strange appearance even to eyes used to Mexican churches.

The citizens of Guanajuato, who appeared happy and carefree, looked prosperous, and there was a businesslike atmosphere everywhere. That evening Peter and Nancy enjoyed the serenading of visitors, by the students of the State College.

The students looked so gay, the men in their big sombreros and the girls in *mantillas*, and they were so friendly in manner, that Peter and Nancy wished they were old enough to go to college. Then, they said, they would ask Uncle Lee to let them stay at Guanajuato.

THE CITY THAT SILVER MADE

THE city of Guanajuato by morning light presented even a more prosperous and glamorous appearance than it had in the late afternoon of the day before. The blue mountains seemed to shut it in on all sides. The side streets ran down into the main street, like hillside streams joining a valley river. The houses on the steep hills seemed to be climbing as if for a better view of the valley. The MacLarens had slept well, for the night had been refreshingly cool and free from mosquitoes.

Wandering about after breakfast they came to some large stone carvings of frogs in one part of the city.

Uncle Lee said, "The name of the town, Guanajuato, means 'Hill of Frogs.' Until now the frogs have failed to materialize."

Nancy enjoyed looking up at the various houses. They were, for the most part, one-story, stucco houses, but they had been painted lovely colors, pink, blue, green, or yellow. The citizens evidently loved color, for their clothes were very gay. The peons bringing their produce to market invariably wore bright red serapes. Brilliant flowers decorated every home, every plaza, and every promenade. Even the prison was covered by a riot of flowers.

James Sawders

A HILLSIDE STREET OF GUANAJUATO

"Would you like to visit the prison?" Uncle Lee asked.

Peter said, "I'd rather see the silver mine this afternoon."

"I vote for the silver mine, too," Nancy decided quickly.

The mine of Pinguico was some distance from the town.

Uncle Lee stood for a long time with Nancy on the veranda of the main building at the mine. From it they could look out upon the brown roads across the plain and the little towns miles away. Men trudging along under huge sombreros or riding what appeared at that distance to be toy donkeys, faded out gradually against the shimmering sky.

The superintendent gave Peter permission to descend into the mine.

Uncle Lee seemed glad to stay on the veranda with Nancy. Peter jubilantly climbed into the crude iron bucket and it was let down into the shaft. The first shaft into which he descended with the men was probably a thousand feet deep. It seemed much deeper to Peter, and he tried to fight down the sense of panic he felt in the damp darkness. He was greatly relieved when they got out of the bucket, and he stumbled along behind the men. They arrived at a gallery where other miners were working in pairs, cutting out rock and ore with chisels and sledges. The man to whose care Peter was entrusted wore leather soles tied to his feet, a loin cloth, and a very large sombrero.

"To keep the sun off, I suppose," Peter joked.

The man not only understood Peter's gesture but his language as well.

"To keep the silver off," the miner replied. "I've been to Texas. I worked there one summer in the oil fields," he added to explain his knowledge of English.

Peter saw the reason for the sombrero later on when a shower of ore, which had been loosened by a pick, tumbled down. The miner who spoke English explained to Peter that much of the ore was broken loose by means of dynamite. He said a hole was made with an automatic drill; a stick of dynamite was thrust into the hole, and the dynamite was set off by a lighted fuse.

Peter looked at the sample of ore the miner handed him. It was flecked with gold and silver and a metal which had a burnished appearance.

"Copper," declared the man.

It was a wonderful experience, but Peter was glad to return to the surface and to find Uncle Lee and Nancy waiting in the sunlight.

"Now we are going to see what becomes of the ore you mined, Peter," Nancy teased. "I suppose you helped load that iron bucket that is just coming up."

The bucket that Nancy indicated was dumped out on an iron screen made of railroad rails. Expert workers broke up the ore, throwing out the ordinary rock. A really sizable hill was formed entirely of discarded rock.

The ore was now loaded on a train and taken to the stamp mill. Like most stamp mills, this particular one was built on the side of a steep hill. The ore was dumped in at the top and, as it went down the many chutes, it was separated from the dross.

"It's the noisiest place in the world," Nancy complained. "But of course a stamp mill would have to be noisy since it's breaking up rocks."

Ewing Galloway

A STAMP MILL

The biggest stones were cracked open with great sledges wielded by muscular men. The medium-sized stones were sent along broad leather belts where men picked out the ones that seemed to be worthless.

The iron stamping machines weighed a good many tons. They came down upon the small stones several times a second, crushing them to powder. When water was added, the result was a mortarlike mixture. It went into iron cylinders.

The process was repeated again and again. The last treatment, with zinc shavings, resulted in the settling of a metal which was half silver and half gold. In a locked room this metal was melted and made into bricks, worth over a thousand dollars each.

"My, they are heavy!" Peter exclaimed as he lifted one end of a brick.

"Two to four bricks are considered a good load for a donkey," Uncle Lee reminded him.

"I don't think I'll try to carry one," Peter said.

He watched the miners coming out of the shaft. Every one was searched for concealed ore. The men looked very tired and dirty.

"Nothing today," decided the young American who searched the miners. "Sometimes they hide ore in their shoes, their hats, or even their hair. And there used to be a good many bandits in these hills who held up our men on their way to town with shipments. But Guanajuato is pretty tame nowadays."

Peter and Nancy had found it anything but tame. For them it had been both strange and interesting.

A CITY OF CHURCHES

"THE name of a pure-bred Zapotec Indian is the most revered name in all Mexico—Benito Juarez!" Doctor Caine was visiting with the MacLarens as they sat in the pleasant living room which was warmed by a stove. "Next to him is, perhaps, Porfirio Diaz. Juarez was the great liberator, and Diaz was the most famous ruler. You are going right into their country."

"Then we're going to visit in Oaxaca. I know how to pronounce it." Peter repeated, "Wah-hah-cah! We'll visit the town and the state, too. Was Diaz a full-bred Zapotec Indian, too?"

"No," Doctor Caine replied. "His mother had Mixtec Indian blood. You must remember him for having kept Mexico in comparative peace for thirty years. He it was who built the railroads and opened up the country to foreign capital. But we're concerned with the Zapotecs at present. Show Peter and Nancy the location of the state of Oaxaca, Mr. MacLaren. The map is on the table."

Uncle Lee pointed out the borders of the state, indicating that it extended from the jungles of Tehuantepec on the Pacific to the cordillera, or long range of mountains on the north and east.

The MacLarens made the trip to Oaxaca by train.

Near Puebla dust poured in through windows that gave a view of Popocatepetl and Malinzín. The sky was azure, the mountain tops snow-white, but the land through which the train went was a dull brown.

Old forts that now were manor houses appeared on the horizon. Uncle Lee pointed out some graceful stone bridges that had been built by the Spaniards. On the brown landscape appeared numerous churches built by the Dominican friars in the sixteenth century. The domes were tiled in steel and silver. It was those friars, Uncle Lee declared, who had established potteries, one or two of which were still in use.

One station at which the train stopped was famous for the silver-inlaid spurs of blue steel that all riders admired. Another station claimed fame for its tamales. They were offered by venders through the car windows, and the tracks were strewn with the discarded cornhusks in which the tamales had been wrapped.

Glancing out, Peter remarked that there were soldiers on top of the express car ahead, and he experienced a thrill at the thought of possible bandits. But when he learned that the express car contained ice packed in mats, and bags of rice, he was not excited.

By noon, as the train sped onward, palms and banana plants began to appear. The fences were made of organ-pipe cacti. Some of the fences were so tall that they nearly hid the tiny

Ewing Galloway

A CACTUS FENCE

houses of the natives who stood in their yards
to watch the train go by. Peddlers offered cactus
buds at car windows as a delicacy. Peter bought
a few, but they tasted, so Nancy observed, just
as one would expect cactus to taste.

The pottery toys offered by the venders were
cleverly made. There were birds, muleteers, bull-
fighters, and donkeys, all very lifelike. There
were the usual pig banks.

The brown country was left behind. Rims of
bare brown rocks began to enclose a valley, a
green valley with a watercourse. Then the rocky

rims rose to mountain heights as the train entered Temollin Canyon. The train ran forty miles through a gorge as impressive as the Royal Gorge in Colorado.

"The gateway into the state of Oaxaca!" Uncle Lee announced. "Now you can see how it was possible for the Zapotec Indians to remain independent during President Carranza's term."

Halfway through the gorge the train stopped at a mountain inn. Uncle Lee called it the Chinaman's. Peter and Nancy were to remember it as a clean, delightful place where pigeons fluttered over the tables from the rafters above, and parrots screeched from their cages. The food they ate was clean and good, and refreshing mountain breezes blew through the dining room.

Back in the train the MacLarens dozed to the steady hum of the wheels. Once Peter roused to call Nancy's attention to a burned roof, the result of a bandit raid. Buildings of adobe, tiles, and stone, Nancy thought, were not easy to burn.

The country was very poor now. The women who came to sell produce offered stunted ears of corn and very small oranges. Even the bananas and watermelons were small. In the dry fields men plowed with wooden plows drawn by oxen. Their garments fluttered in the wind.

Long, monotonous hours passed. The last range of hills was crossed. The tracks of the train led down into a beautiful valley.

Small towns with garrisons seemed to pass in

review, and on the crests of the hills were Indian
villages. In front of ranch houses women stood
in lines with woven-reed baskets of coffee. They
were waiting for the paymaster of the hacienda.

Oaxaca at last! The station was full of noisy,
good-natured Indians. Uncle Lee hailed a cab
which once had been the carriage of some
wealthy Spaniard.

As the stately carriage rattled over the cobblestones, Peter and Nancy remarked on the number and beauty of the churches they passed.

"You told us once, Uncle Lee," Nancy said,
"that Oaxaca had the reputation of being the
most godly place in Mexico. If churches mean
godliness, then it surely is godly."

The hotel rooms to which the MacLarens were
taken were large, cool, and comfortably furnished. The food was delicious and of wide
variety.

Uncle Lee took Peter and Nancy to the plaza
on that first evening. A band played until
twenty-one o'clock, which marked bedtime in
Oaxaca just as it did in other Mexican towns.
This was nine o'clock in American time. The
great cathedral on the plaza had a most remarkable facade, embellished with fine sculpture.

"It must be wonderful inside," Nancy said,
thinking of the golden cathedral of Puebla.

Uncle Lee told her the cathedral had been pil-
laged so often that nothing remained of its original altar or priceless paintings.

The plaza was alive with color, sparkle, and noise. There were army officers in attractive uniforms, riders in tight breeches trimmed with silver buttons, Indian women wearing gay rebozos, and pretty girls guarded by their *duennas*, or chaperones. Occasionally a young man rode by on a well-groomed horse with jingling bridle.

In the morning Nancy woke to the melodious chiming of bells. She went to call Uncle Lee and Peter and found them in the corridor laughing over the size of a key the hotel owner was showing them. It was so large and heavy that Nancy could hardly lift it.

However, when she went out with Uncle Lee and Peter after breakfast, she could understand the necessity for the big key. The old houses were low and massive, and the timbered doors had thick steel bars. Those houses had been designed to withstand earthquakes and mobs. Uncle Lee said that in the past both had been only too common in Oaxaca.

"The church bells are gentle enough," Nancy suggested, remembering the sweetness of the chimes that had awakened her.

"The bells you heard were probably of gold and silver and bronze," Uncle Lee remarked. "When one says 'silver chimes' or 'gold chimes' here, he means literally just what he says."

"The richest state in Mexico when the Spaniards came!" Peter mused. "I suppose they mined out all the gold and silver."

"That's where you're mistaken," Uncle Lee said. "This is still a rich country. The deposits about Oaxaca have scarcely been touched. Indians still drift in with raw gold, not in nuggets but in balls or plates. Some of this gold has white streaks of silver in it. But these Indians never tell where they get it."

"I don't blame them," Peter declared with some heat. "Why should they trust people? Doctor Caine said that in the time of Cortez many friars hid the gold and silver vessels in the walls of houses. Some of the friars died without revealing the hiding places. Sometimes when houses are torn down, hidden gold is found in the walls. Doctor Caine says, too, that bandits and looters often scraped the gold off the church decorations."

"I'll show you the church Doctor Caine was probably thinking of," Uncle Lee promised.

He led Peter and Nancy to the great church of Santo Domingo with its barrel-arch ceiling. The ceiling had been beautifully sculptured and had gold decorations, as did the walls. Looters with ladders had scraped off the gold as high as they could reach.

What was left made the McLarens stare in awed wonder. Peter and Nancy were thankful that some of that shining splendor remained.

AMONG THE ZAPOTECS

THE hotel manager had told the MacLarens that the trails leading out from Oaxaca took travelers into little towns that could be found on no map. A friend of his who had been in this country told of seeing great forests and jungles. In them were many snakes, bright-colored birds, and wild hogs. He spoke also of the alligators in the bayous and of jaguars who came close to the campfires out of curiosity. Deer drank at the rivers and were not afraid of men.

The manager was very proud of Oaxaca state which he said covered thirty-five thousand square miles and in which a million people lived. He recommended the market in Oaxaca as the place where one could see interesting types of people.

The next morning was market day and the MacLarens were up at dawn to watch the mule trains that came in from every part of the state. They saw little men from the jungles and tall men from the hill country. At the market an intelligent Zapotec who had learned English told Uncle Lee of his village, Jauchitan, which he said was the home of the Tree of the Little Hands.

"The center of the flower," Uncle Lee explained to Peter and Nancy as they stood at the fruit stall looking at the fine guavas, "is in the form of a little hand with the fingers curved inward. The

color is a lovely red. The Zapotecs as well as the
Mixtecs venerate it. Many years ago a Mixtec
chief refused to send a tribute of these flowers to
Montezuma. The great Aztec chief took thousands of lives as a punishment."

The cochineal industry was begun at another
village near by, the young Zapotec informed Uncle
Lee. This little village of Cuilapan sold the little
insects of which red dye is made, traders carrying them into Guatemala and to the Canary
Islands. But today even the natives of the village use aniline dyes when dyeing their blankets.

Then the young Zapotec told them about the
rubber country around Oaxaca. Peter and
Nancy thought they would like to see the two-
wheeled carts drawn by oxen and loaded with
cans, much like our large milk cans, which carried
the rubber latex, or milky fluid, to market.

"This is not like the rubber of northern Mexico," interrupted Uncle Lee. "There the guayule
industry is becoming more and more important.
Guayule is a shrub which produces rubber.
Workers pull the shrubs, knock off the dirt, and
load them on burros until the little animals are
nearly hidden. The burros take the shrubs to
stations in the desert where they are baled,
hauled to the nearest railroad, and shipped to
the factory. Since the roads have been improved,
large sums of money had been invested in guayule factories, and new towns have sprung up
near the fields."

Peter and Nancy wandered away from Uncle
Lee and the market. They saw little children
lifted from great baskets containing vegetables
and fruit, in which they had ridden on the long
trip from some faraway village. Many mothers
carried babies on their backs as they trudged
along, and older brothers carried small brothers
about on their shoulders. Going to market was
not just business for the man of the house. It
was a big social event in which the entire family
took part. It was something to talk about after
the long journey home.

Vegetables of all kinds, potatoes, tomatoes,
peppers, onions, rice, sugar cane, and corn were
displayed in abundance. There was plenty of
coffee, vanilla, and cacao. The flowers were
gorgeous and the medicinal herbs strange and
interesting. One lad offered oxhorns for sale,
and hummingbird bodies as charms insuring safe
journeys.

Judging from the general produce Peter and
Nancy decided that the farm lands in the valleys
between the blue hills must be very rich.

"What do you suppose the stores in Oaxaca
sell, Peter?" Nancy asked. "There seems to be
everything here that anyone would need."

"Uncle Lee says the stores deal in imported
goods only," Peter answered. "There is a central market, too, that happens to be built by an
American firm. But I imagine most people
patronize this market."

Ewing Galloway

RAINCOATS MADE OF SISAL FIBERS

Food seemed to be one of the most important products of the market. A woman was selling hot tortillas from a basket. They smelled unbelievably good. Some of the food was being cooked in little earthen pots over small charcoal fires, food hot with chili. The coffee beans, rice, and vegetable beans were spread on mats on the ground.

One woman was selling raincoats made of sisal fibers. Nancy remarked that they looked much more like mats than coats. However, they seemed to be popular with the natives.

James Sawders

SERAPES FOR SALE!

The serape sellers sat by themselves. Each family had a pile of white and red, and black and red, and gray and red blankets. Eagle and tiger patterns were common. Peter had seen several of these men trotting in earlier, each under what appeared to be a back-breaking load of the blankets. At night the unsold serapes would have to be carried back up the trails to the venders' native villages.

"There is something interesting about the serapes in this market." Uncle Lee joined Peter

and Nancy as they stood admiring a fine red
and white blanket. "I think this is the place to
buy our serapes to take home. They come from
the village of Teotitlan."

"They look much the same as other serapes
to me," Peter decided.

"But they aren't." Uncle Lee grinned. "In
Teotitlan there is a cave, and there is a good
story connected with that cave. One day the
Spirit of the Shadows spoke to the men of old
who were gathered there. The Spirit of the
Shadows decided that from that time forward
the village of Teotitlan was to devote its time
to weaving serapes. A neighboring village was
to make pottery. Another one was to weave
robes. Still another was to weave cloth. The
Spirit of the Shadows was very wise. He wanted
the various tribesmen to be neighborly, and to be
neighborly they must have a reason for meeting.
Thus each was required to make something the
other needed and wanted."

"So it was really the Spirit of the Shadows
that started the markets," Nancy put in. "Men
had to come together to trade, and, of course, that
meant visiting and exchanging ideas."

"Then these markets were not introduced by
the Spaniards," Peter decided. "They must have
been here long before Cortez came."

"They were," Uncle Lee said. "The plaza, too,
is the result of the need to barter. Of course, you
have noticed that each Indian village is built

around a plaza. Once it was a dusty, treeless square. It was the Empress Carlotta who influenced the Indians to plant trees in their plazas. That was the beginning of the beautification of plazas. It was followed by the planting of flowers and the building of fountains."

Oaxaca, an industrial and commercial center, lay on a plain backed against the mountains. Its houses were low and massive and earthquake-resisting and were built on level ground. But all the roads out of the city led upward. The educated Zapotec Indian advised Uncle Lee to take Peter and Nancy on horseback along the road to Teotitlan to see the great Tree of Tule. After lunch the MacLarens set out.

The tree proved to be a cypress 170 feet high and so great of girth that thirty persons with fingertips touching could barely encircle it.

As the MacLarens drew rein under the tree, the sound of a trumpet came to their ears. Looking up they saw a small church, and on the battlements appeared a soldier with a silver trumpet. Uncle Lee said that the tradition of a trumpet call had come from the ancestors of the present Zapotecs, but no one knew its significance. The sounds were strained and mournful.

The Zapotecs were quite different from other Mexicans, Peter and Nancy felt. Of course, they spoke their own dialect, and in many villages Spanish was not understood at all. Nancy noticed that a Zapotec woman wore her rebozo differently. Instead of carrying it around her shoulders, she always wound it into a turban, with a corner of it hanging down behind. Zapotec noses were more beaklike than Aztec noses, Peter decided. He also observed that Zapotec chins were less receding than Aztec chins.

"And there is another difference," Uncle Lee said. "The Zapotec is loyal to his village, his own immediate group, instead of to his state. He carries on his own wars and resents any interference. There are feuds back in the hills that the government can't control. The dead are buried secretly and the wounded are hidden. The Indian keeps his affairs to himself. He wants no white man mixed up in what he considers his own business."

On the following morning Uncle Lee hired a taxi to visit Mitla, more interesting to archeologists than to any one else.

"No one," Uncle Lee said, "has been able to interpret the story the ruins hold."

The plains were dry, and although it was early spring, plowing was under way. The wooden plows, drawn by oxen, merely scratched the surface of the soil. At intervals as they drove back to town the MacLarens saw castor-bean plots.

Vehicles with solid wooden wheels creaked along the road. Some of these wagons had woven rush canopies through which could be seen the blue sky above.

Many fences were made of organ cacti. The

Ewing Galloway

CART WITH SOLID WOODEN WHEELS

men and boys working in the fields or driving the oxen, all wore heavy gray felt sombreros. Lines of women marched along the roadside carrying baskets of produce on their heads. The driver said that there were often long lines of these women walking into town on the railway tracks, carrying grain. It was cheaper to carry the produce than to send it by freight.

The car passed an old church with a series of dome roofs and soon Mitla came in view.

The ruins were massive and mostly covered with what looked like jigsaw puzzles in relief. There were insets of stone that Uncle Lee said were cut from a lava rock of yellowish tint. Peter stared at the uncarved lintels. They must

Ewing Galloway

WALLS OF THE TEMPLE AT MITLA

have weighed tons. Nancy called to her brother
to look at the exquisite designs carved on some
of the blocks of stone.

"Was Mitla a town?" Nancy asked Uncle Lee.

"Mitla means 'resting place for souls,'" Uncle
Lee explained. "Perhaps Mitla refers to the
world beyond."

Peter walked through the subterranean pas-
sages. Nancy attempted to find something in the
inscriptions that she might understand. Uncle
Lee bought a copper axhead that a vender insisted he had found in a tomb in Mitla. Uncle

Lee told Peter when he finally emerged from his explorations that it was possible that the ancient Zapotecs knew the secret of tempering copper.

Peter, however, was more interested in the ornate passageways. A guide had told him that there were a million stone slabs, about an inch thick, in the mosaic decorations. These little pieces had been hewn from a quarry and shaped with stone hatchets. In his mind Peter saw countless men fashioning the small stones, and others hewing out the six large columns that were in the Hall of Monoliths. These columns, three feet in diameter and fourteen feet high, had once supported the ceiling and roof of what might have been a palace.

"Such workers should be remembered," Peter thought, and hoped that some day the archeologists would be able to read the story of the very earliest Zapotecs.

MEXICO'S SECOND LARGEST CITY

THE train that was to carry the MacLarens into Guadalajara stopped at Irapuato just long enough for them to buy boxes of delicious strawberries.

"I've always wanted to be able to eat a great big box of strawberries out of season," Peter declared as he seated himself opposite Uncle Lee and Nancy in the train. "They say that here in Irapuato you can buy strawberries fresh from the plants every month in the year. My, but these are big, wonderful berries!"

But as Peter continued to eat, his expression changed, for the big berries had been on top, and they gradually decreased in size. Peter grinned good-naturedly.

"The Mexicans are like the Americans," he declared.

The MacLarens knew that all three of the main railroads ran into Guadalajara, and they were not surprised to get off the train and find themselves in a rich, fine city. It was the capital of Jalisco, one of the richest states in Mexico.

Peter and Nancy were soon out on the streets after getting their baggage settled in their hotel rooms. The business section was delightful, for the pedestrians were always out of the sun except when crossing the streets. Great stone or adobe archways that Uncle Lee called *portales* covered the sidewalk. Everywhere there were the famous porous clay jars for sale. Uncle Lee said that, because of the evaporation, water would keep cold in them even on a warm day.

Dinnertime in a fine restaurant proved to be a most enjoyable hour. And when the lights came on, there were huge electrical signs such as Peter and Nancy associated with home. Uncle Lee secured a cab to show the children the city with its many plazas. Later they returned to the central plaza to hear a good band concert.

Nancy was awakened at dawn next day by the peal of countless bells. Down below a policeman was blowing a whistle. An electric streetcar sounded a gong as it pounded over the tracks. Dogs were barking, roosters crowing. Nancy tried to snuggle down for another nap, but venders began to shout their wares. A strolling young man who chanced to be passing began to sing. An old man's voice broke into a singsong wail, "*Leche, leche!*"

Nancy got up, bathed, dressed, and went out on the little balcony off her room. Evidently that cry, "Leche, leche!" meant nothing more than "Milk, milk!" for across the street a girl came out with a clay jar. The old man who had been wailing, poured some milk from one of two big cans his mule carried. Then he went on down the street. At the same time a boy driving a flock of turkeys came up the street. The turkeys marched along, their necks making a sharp, jerking motion with each step. The boy flicked at them with a stick at the end of which was a piece of string.

In the hall Nancy encountered Uncle Lee and Peter who insisted on breakfast before viewing the street scenes with her.

By the time the MacLarens had finished breakfast and had come out on Nancy's balcony, the sidewalks of Guadalajara were alive with workers. *Señoritas,* fashionably attired in bright thin dresses, clicked past on high heels. Their stockings were silk, their hair bobbed, their hands manicured in the latest style. Young men in flannels carried sticks and smoked native cigarettes. The girls and the men might easily have come from Hollywood.

Strolling out to see the town, Uncle Lee pointed out the colossal prison. He quoted the local saying, "They built the jail big enough to hold everybody in town, as a warning." He then added, "And the quickest way to get into jail is to argue with a traffic cop."

The MacLarens went window-shopping. Nancy stopped often to look at pieces of pottery in the old Aztec designs. Uncle Lee told her that many of these pieces of pottery had been made by Mexican Indians who lived in the small neighboring town of Tonala. The art of pottery making and decoration had been passed from father to son since the days of the Aztecs. Peter laughed over

Ewing Galloway

A FAMILY OF ARTISTS

a display of caricatures made of clay by one of
the famous Panduro brothers, Indian artists. Not
only had the artist made a statuette of Obregón;
he also had made one of Henry Ford. Uncle Lee
was most interested in the work that interpreted
life in Mexico: tiny pack mules, market women,
and *vaqueros*, or cowboys, on horses. These sculp-
tors had never taken lessons, but their ancestors
had worked in clay before the Spaniards came.

As the members of a small band came march-
ing along the street making lively music, Nancy's

eyes sparkled. She cried, "Music everywhere! Oh, there's another organ-grinder. That must be the tenth we've seen today. How do all the organ-grinders make a living?"

"Strange as it may seem," Uncle Lee explained, "organ-grinders are subsidized by a fund that was willed to the city to insure free hand-organ music always. As for the bands that we see, it is quite customary for a man to hire a band to celebrate any stroke of luck he may have. Often he strolls past the homes of his friends with his band and boasts of his achievements."

Near the post office the MacLarens saw a man writing on a typewriter set up on a box. He was a public scribe, they learned. He would write any kind of letter anyone wanted written.

As in other Mexican cities, there was a splendid cathedral. It rose against the sky, its twin towers visible for miles. On feast days long strings of lights illuminated the towers. It was in this fine old cathedral that the MacLarens viewed a great painting, Murillo's "The Assumption of the Virgin." Uncle Lee said that it had been given to the cathedral by the king of Spain in return for help in the Peninsular War. Many men went to his aid from Guadalajara, and legend tells that money was raised for the king by melting gold and silver plate and candlesticks from the cathedral.

In the public library were some very valuable manuscripts. The librarian complained that only too often the ancient histories of Mexico were set aside for such modern things as radios and motion pictures.

The stores sold modern goods. A merchant, Nancy observed, never expected a customer to carry a large package. He invariably called a street porter who trotted behind the customer with the package all the way home. There seemed to be many wealthy customers, and Uncle Lee said there were many families in the city who owned heirlooms of gold and silver plate.

The next day Uncle Lee secured a car for a two-day trip to Lake Pátzcuaro in the state of Michoacán. As the MacLarens drove out of Guadalajara they discussed the interesting city they were leaving behind them.

"How old is Guadalajara, Uncle Lee?" Nancy asked.

"The town was laid out about 1530, I believe," Uncle Lee replied. "The word Guadalajara is from the Moorish and means 'river of rocks.' The king of Spain gave the town its coat of arms in 1539. By 1560 it had become important, but it was a center for the Indian slave trade. The slaves were forced to work in the mines, and many a fortune in this city dates back to that period."

The ride was pleasant, and after several hours the party arrived at Pátzcuaro. Peter and Nancy were delighted with the little town perched on a hill overlooking the thirteen-mile-long lake.

"Pátzcuaro means 'a joyous place,'" Uncle Lee

Luiz Marquez

THE FISHING BOATS WERE SIMPLE DUGOUTS

informed them as they left their small hotel and wandered down to the lake. "This whole region is noted for its beauty and serenity, and this section is called the Paradise of Mexico by the Mexicans themselves."

The people did seem happy! Women, picturesque in their wide skirts pleated around the waist, with tops opening like fans over handwoven sashes, walked by with lovely water jars on their heads.

"These Tarascan Indians are an extremely high type and possessed great culture before the

Luiz Marquez

THE INDIANS USE THEIR FISH NETS FOR SAILS

coming of the white man," Uncle Lee told them. "Now they are simple fishermen and farmers. They are looked upon as being very honest and straightforward, and they are highly regarded throughout Mexico.

"President Cardenas himself is a Tarascan, and his private home is in Lago just a few miles up this shore."

Peter and Nancy had been watching the fleet of fishing boats which were coming in. As they came closer it could be seen that they were simple dugouts, some of them holding as many as thirty men.

"Look at the sails!" Nancy cried. "Thin, gauzy sails that you can see through! They look like nets."

"They are nets," Uncle Lee agreed. "The Indians use their fish nets for sails. It seems strange that anything so full of holes can be used to propel a boat over the waters of the lake, but strangely enough it can."

As the darkness settled over the lake the Mac-Larens went to their hotel knowing that they would never find a place more unspoiled and peaceful. This mood lingered to the next morning when they went down to the shore to take a last look at the lake and to watch the fleet go out for another day of fishing.

On the way back to Guadalajara the Mac-Larens saw many cornfields but few small farms. Most of the land was in huge estates owned by the wealthy. In fact, the haciendas were really quite like the medieval feudal estates, and the government had just begun to be interested in cutting up the large tracts into small farms for the masses.

Early the next morning the MacLarens boarded the Southern Pacific train for Mazatlán on the western coast. Situated just across the gulf from Lower California, it had become a popular winter resort.

While Uncle Lee was busy at the hotel, Peter

and Nancy wandered past the gay pink stucco houses and on to the picturesque lookout places, built of stone and perched high on the cliffs above the sea.

Nancy thought it was a strange sight to see factories, sawmills, and foundries where there were so many beautiful, graceful palms, and elephant-ear banana trees.

Before returning to Guadalajara, Peter and Nancy dined with Uncle Lee in the open patio of a quaint Old World cafe. Here they stayed until evening, that they might see the breakers of Olas Atlas Bay, lighted with phosphorus and tumbling against the sea wall.

IN THE TROPICS

THE MacLarens returned to Mexico City from
Guadalajara by train but only for an overnight stay. Uncle Lee disposed of his car and
bought tickets on the Mexican National Railway
to Veracruz. Regretfully he announced that
the time had come to leave the high plateau with
its cool, delightful climate for the tropical heat
of the Gulf coast.

The descent from the great plateau must have
been a difficult engineering feat, for the railway
line zigzagged back and forth for miles.

Sometimes it seemed as though the train were
teetering on the brink of a precipice, and once
Peter and Nancy looked out of the window at a
town two thousand feet below them, the town
of Maltrata.

One familiar landmark remained, the symmet-
rical snow-capped summit of Mount Orizaba. It
seemed to be very far away. Even when the Mac-
Larens stayed overnight in the town of Orizaba,
the mountain seemed to be at a great distance
from town.

There was no time in which to visit Orizaba's
large plantations or cotton mills, for early in the
morning the MacLarens were descending to Cor-
doba. This little town lay almost directly below
Orizaba, but it took eighteen miles of winding

road and tunnels to get there. Peter and Nancy soon realized that they were in tropical country again. The train passed through jungles where orchids hung in the trees. Banana plants rose above the tangled bushes, and once in a while a coffee plantation appeared. A blackbird sat in a pink locust tree. The sun shone on red-flowered trees deep in the jungles.

Their journey ended at Veracruz where the Mexican railway also ended.

"We really came in the back door of Veracruz," Uncle Lee declared. "The front entrance is the sea."

Peter and Nancy knew that Cortez had landed in Veracruz on Good Friday and had given the place a name appropriate to the day—the True Cross.

The MacLarens drove about the city and were impressed with the industry of the port. Uncle Lee said the city had once been a very unhealthful place where a traveler had been almost certain to contract yellow fever. Now, however, it was quite healthful even though the heat did make one feel as though he were running a temperature.

How gay the town was! The houses were painted in bright yellows, reds, and blues. The windows of the ground floor had iron bars like those of a prison. There were few chimneys as all over Mexico the people use charcoal for cooking, and it was too hot to have a fire for warmth.

Ewing Galloway

NATIVE WOMEN OFFERING LINENS FOR SALE

Along the streets were Mexican women selling embroidered linens which they had made. Nancy liked the work so much that she decided to buy a scarf for her mother.

Many of the women on the street were dressed in black, with lace shawls over their heads. The men from the country had hats with brims a foot wide and trimmed with bands of silver and gold as thick as a finger.

The harbor was a modern one, and ships were loading and unloading onto concrete docks by means of cranes. Travelers were coming up gangplanks from ships. Many travelers visiting Mexico begin their journey at Veracruz, Uncle Lee explained, and a large proportion of exports and imports are handled through Veracruz.

"Everything but oil, I suppose," Peter volunteered.

"Right!" Uncle Lee agreed. "Tampico is the oil port."

Driving into the country they passed thickets of bamboo, cane, mahogany and ebony trees, and vines which bore the vanilla beans. Mockingbirds whistled at them as they passed. Some Indian women brought pineapples to the car. Uncle Lee bought some, and later they ate them with a spoon. Of course, they were fresher and riper than any sold in the States.

By morning the heat of Veracruz seemed only a myth. A cold wind began to blow. Uncle Lee said it was called a *norte*. The plaza was deserted by the sunshine-loving Mexicans. It was a dusty plaza, but the MacLarens' hotel faced it, and it was interesting if not beautiful.

The MacLarens sailed by boat from Veracruz to Tampico, a pleasant journey for Peter and Nancy. Uncle Lee sat with a glum American who had oil interests in Tampico and who was much concerned because, according to the 1917 constitution, the Mexican Government guaranteed to the owner of the surface, subsoil rights only on lands acquired before 1917 and definitely tagged for oil purposes.

Ewing Galloway

A BUSY MARKET PLACE IN TAMPICO

"We've built the town," the American oil man growled. "Why, down here even the natives call Tampico *Gringolandia*. We're gringos, all right, but what prosperity would there be without us?"

Peter grinned at Nancy.

"The oil Uncle Lee uses in his car is probably from Tampico," he remarked.

Near the coast oil derricks rose against the bright blue sky. A pall of black smoke hung over Tampico from a recent fire in an oil well. There was a greasy smell in the air.

Uncle Lee said that the wildcat period of oil exploitation had seen Tampico grow from a dozen mud huts to a modern city of paved streets. Nowadays there were many American homes, and modern sanitation.

Dinner in Tampico meant American food and an American atmosphere.

"Why should we call ourselves Americans, as though the United States were all of North America?" queried Nancy, as dessert was served. "Mexico, and Canada, too, are also parts of America."

"You have asked a good question, Nancy, and one we are not likely to think of until we are out of the United States," said Uncle Lee. "You see, when the Europeans wanted to speak of the people in North America, they could easily say 'Mexicans' or 'Canadians,' but they could not make an adjective of the name United States, and so they came to call the people of the United States Americans."

The MacLarens returned to Veracruz and then went to Córdoba in order to take the Mexican National Railroad down to the Isthmus of Tehuantepec. Peter and Nancy were deeply impressed by the dense jungle through which the train moved. Gangs of men were constantly at work to keep the plant life from covering the tracks. Fruit grew so plentifully that all of it could not be used. Oranges that hung ripe on trees would drop to the ground to rot. Pine-

apples were offered through the train windows
for a few cents. Uncle Lee pointed out the
various beautiful palm trees that rose from the
tangled masses of foliage.

The valley gave way to hills, the hills to
meadowlands. There were cattle grazing on the
rich bottoms, and there were gardens near neat
houses. At one station Peter saw some boys who
reminded him of the neighbor boys back home.

"They certainly are not Mexicans," Peter declared.

"They are Americans," Uncle Lee agreed,
"descendants of Mormons who came here from
Utah years ago."

The train reached Santa Lucrecia before midnight, and the MacLarens went directly to the
hotel. Uncle Lee insisted that Nancy be given
a room with screens and also a mosquito net
canopy for her bed.

"The town is less than a hundred feet above
sea level," Uncle Lee explained. "The air is
nearly always hot and heavy, as it is tonight.
By daylight you'll see that the houses are made
of sheet-iron and thatch for the most part. They
have to be built upon piles to be safe from floods
and wild animals."

But Peter and Nancy were too tired to care
much about the town. They were glad to be
shown to their rooms and to fall asleep on string
beds. Uncle Lee could not sleep because the
partitions of his room did not reach the ceiling

and he could hear the sounds from all over the crude hotel. But no sounds could keep Peter and Nancy awake.

In the morning the three MacLarens met on the hotel porch. They were in the midst of a banana grove.

"We're in the narrowest part of Mexico!" Peter exclaimed, looking at a map. "The chain of mountains stretching from Alaska down the Pacific coast almost disappears here."

The train that the MacLarens took sped southward across the isthmus. Several Tehuantepec women in the train wore their national head-dress, the *huipil.* It was an elaborate creation of lace and ruffles, starched stiff with part of it hanging down the back. Uncle Lee said that a woman wearing a huipil and balancing a flower-painted gourd on her head made a very attractive picture, even though her feet were bare.

Nancy was interested in one group of women in the train. Each woman wore a skirt made of a square of cloth wrapped about her waist. Her blouse was sleeveless. In her smooth, black hair she wore red flowers and about her throat a necklace. Peter could hardly be convinced that some of those necklaces were made of actual gold pieces from the United States.

The houses all through the jungle were of flimsy construction. There was no need for substantial buildings. The people seemed happy. The food they needed was close at hand, and there was no necessity for hard labor. A few men and women worked in the fields of sugar cane. They walked behind crude plows drawn by oxen.

"We're coming into Tehuantepec," Uncle Lee announced presently. "It's the largest town on the isthmus."

The large town proved to be an Indian village of a great Zapotec family, with sandy lanes leading between groups of houses. There were some cobbled streets. A shallow river ran through the valley in which the town was located, and here the townspeople bathed and did their washing.

There was a great proportion of women in the market place. Uncle Lee said that so many of the men had been killed in warfare that the women had learned to do most of the work. They grew most of the sugar cane and sold it in the market.

LAND OF VOLCANOES AND COFFEE

THE MacLarens rode in a cart drawn by oxen to a small railroad town in order to take the Pan-American train. It was not much of a train, since it had only a single passenger car attached to a freight.

"Like our Peanut Special back home," Peter observed.

Without hurry or flurry the train made its way along tracks that ran through high jungle plants that often swished against the car windows. Parrots flashed in and out of bamboo thickets, and cockatoos scolded from thick tangles of vegetation.

Then the jungle gave way to arid land full of cactus and mesquite. All day the train crept along, making a little over a hundred miles. All night it rested from its exertions. The MacLarens with other passengers spent the hours in a tiny, hot hotel with no modern accommodations.

Another day's ride in a southeastern direction, and the MacLarens found themselves at sundown in Mariscal on the Mexico-Guatemala border.

The officer who inquired into Uncle Lee's reason for traveling in Guatemala with two young people was most helpful when he learned that

Ewing Galloway

OX-CARTS IN GUATEMALA

the quest was for a knowledge of geography. He found a crude, two-wheeled cart to take the Mac-Larens to Coatepeque where there was a hotel. The cart was drawn by oxen, and the yoke was fastened to the top of the oxen's horns in regulation Spanish style. The wheels were heavy wooden ones that creaked, and the cart, with the MacLarens sitting on the floor, tipped and tilted in the deep sand. The sun was hot.

While Peter and Nancy clung to the fencelike sides of the cart, the oxen waded streams, pushed doggedly through openings in the jungle, and went on over uneven, boggy ground with as little concern as though they were on a hard dirt road. Nor did the insects seem to bother them greatly.

The hotel in Coatepeque was like a simple barracks, but to Peter and Nancy it seemed the very essence of luxury that evening.

Immediately after breakfast next morning the MacLarens started out. All over the country-side they saw sharp-pointed peaks, which Uncle Lee said were volcanoes.

"They're a blessing as well as a bane," he declared. "Lava soil makes good coffee soil. Volcanoes and coffee belong together."

"Evidently bananas belong here, too," Peter decided. "There seems to be an endless number of banana groves—everywhere you look. Are we going to employ our oxcart? It seems to be waiting."

The MacLarens had never visited larger coffee plantations nor more prosperous ones. The trees had been planted in long, parallel rows, the shiny green foliage so thick that each tree seemed to be almost solid. Peter and Nancy knew, from seeing coffee plantations in South America, that the trees had to have a certain amount of protection from the hot sun. Here in Guatemala the shade was furnished by banana plants or sometimes small jungle trees.

The bushes were covered with bright red berries, the color of holly berries, but beanlike in shape. Opening a couple of the berries, the children discovered the familiar white coffee beans, two of them, their flat surfaces together.

Women were picking the berries carefully, putting them into baskets, and carrying the baskets up to the big plantation house where they were to be spread on outdoor floors to dry in the sun. Men kept shoveling the great heaps of coffee beans so that they would dry evenly. The MacLarens watched them for some time, then went to see the old women who, with swift fingers, hulled beans in the shade of their huts.

The owner of this particular plantation was absent, but Uncle Lee chatted with the overseer who told him that the workers received only a few cents a day for their work. But he assured the shocked MacLaren children that the laborers were also given fifty pounds of corn and beans each month, as well as a half-pound of salt.

"We're returning to Mariscal the way we came," Uncle Lee decided as the trio rode back to the hotel. "From there we'll go to Guatemala City. Now don't ask questions!"

Peter and Nancy sensed that a surprise awaited them. Going back along the road over which they had come, they found it a decidedly busy place. There was a constant procession of sturdy Indians, in colorful homespun garments, carrying produce to market. Donkeys struggled along under heavy loads, men carried packs, and even young girls supported large earthen vessels of water on their heads.

"Are all the people in Guatemala Indians?"
Peter inquired.

"There are about twenty different tribes of Indians here," Uncle Lee answered. "Some are descendants of the Toltecs and some are Mayas. I'd estimate that eight out of ten people in Guatemala are of pure Indian blood. The other fifth of the population claims European ancestry. Some of the plantation owners are Germans. They grow coffee, cacao, and sugar cane. The visitors are people from all countries."

"And what kind of Indians are these?" questioned Peter as they met a group of natives wearing kilts.

"Kakichecial Indians," Uncle Lee replied. "They are known as the 'Scotchmen of Central America.'"

As the oxcart bumped along over the uneven stones into Mariscal, a welcoming yell rose above the creaking and rumbling of the wheels. Before the oxen had stopped, Peter and Nancy were out of the cart shouting, "Jimmy! Jimmy Dustin!"

Tall, brown, slim Jimmy Dustin greeted his friends. His blue eyes were merry.

"What's the idea, traveling by oxcart?" he teased. "You'd never see much of Guatemala that way. Don't you know that in the most backward countries you must travel the most modern way? You could have flown directly from Mexico City to Guatemala City. Or you could have gone by water on the Atlantic side

James Sawders

"SCOTCHMEN OF CENTRAL AMERICA"

to Puerto Barrios, or to San José on the Pacific side. Then you could have taken the International Railways which connects the ports with the capital. Well, my plane's waiting for you. Come on! All aboard for Guatemala City!"

Jimmy's airplane arose from lowlands washed by tropic seas. Then he swung the plane inland where the MacLarens could look down on tropical forests, peaceful fields, and meadowlands where cattle grazed and where simple villages of thatched adobe huts nestled in green valleys.

Lakes like blue jewels and mountains with snowcaps appeared on the landscape. The two large cone-shaped volcanoes, Agua and Fuego, came into view and a modern city appeared below. From the plane the city looked like a checkerboard, with low buildings set in a pattern.

The MacLaren party landed safely, took a taxi to the hotel, and planned to spend several days in the capital of Guatemala. After a delicious lunch, Jimmy offered to entertain Peter and Nancy for a short time. The children found the stores delightful. Goods were moderate in price, and they always had the good fortune to find a clerk who could speak English.

"I thought Guatemala was the most out-of-the-way country in the world," Peter remarked. "I didn't think we'd be able to buy so much as a toothbrush."

"It is an out-of-the-way place." Jimmy grinned. "Of course, the All-American Cable Company will take a message from you and get it to the proper address in Minnesota. The Tropical Radio has direct circuits to the United States, and the radio-telephone service is available to all. Some of the Indians in Guatemala have made commendable progress. Many who practice their crafts and sell their products for a living have been educated in the free schools of Guatemala City. Don't look so disappointed. You'll find plenty of primitive life, if that's what you're looking for. See Agua up there?"

Ewing Galloway

AN INDIAN WEAVER IN GUATEMALA

The volcano looked peaceful enough, but its story was a tale of devastation and terror. Jimmy declared that there had been three capitals of Guatemala, the present capital being the third.

The first capital, which was now called the Old City and was inhabited by a few thousand Indians, had been founded by Pedro de Alvarado. With the help of fine architects and expert workmen from Spain, he made it a magnificent city. In 1541 it was destroyed by a flood. The lake in the crater of the volcano Agua broke through

the walls and flooded the city, sweeping away
the work of the builders and causing great mis-
ery. The survivors moved the capital two miles
northeast, and with courage built a new city of
grand palaces and magnificent cathedrals. But
this time Fuego erupted, pouring down a flood of
hot lava on the city and setting the beautiful new
buildings on fire. Where the second capital stood
is the ruined town of Guatemala Antigua, which
means "the ancient." A few thousand Indians
live among its ruins, or close by.

Peter and Nancy marveled at a people that
could build with hope and courage after expe-
riencing such great disasters. The new capital,
Jimmy was saying, had been located twenty
miles from the second capital and had served as
the seat of government since 1779.

"And don't think this capital hasn't had a hard
time," he challenged Peter and Nancy. "It looks
peaceful enough as you walk along the streets
here beside me, but there have been earthquakes,
floods, avalanches, and epidemics in its lifetime.
The Indians believe that the evil spirits are try-
ing to drive the people away from the lovely
surroundings of Agua and Fuego. You'll see
the old cities, and, since I can't take you, I'll
put you in charge of a Clark tour."

"Tourists!" Peter objected.

"Which isn't a bad thing to be," Jimmy declared. "Or maybe you'd rather be on your own
in an oxcart."

A RELIEF MAP

"THERE is no such thing as window-shopping here in Guatemala City," Nancy observed. "It's funny that there are no glass windows in the shops, just wide-open doors. Of course, plate-glass windows wouldn't be very satisfactory in case of an earthquake. I suppose the doors on the inside lead to the home above the shop. It's a convenient arrangement."

"Speaking of doors!" Peter paused before a fine large house of ivory stucco. "Look at the immense door of this house, and the brass knocker. I've been noticing knockers like that all along the street. They're usually of brass or iron and in the form of a human head or hand. And this door has another door cut into it, a smaller one!"

"Jimmy told me about such doors," Nancy informed her brother. "The small door is the family entrance, and the big door swings open to admit a carriage or a car. The door opens on the patio, not into the house. Peter, let's go to the *Mercado Central* on our way back. Uncle Lee says it has the most tropical produce of any market in Central America."

The great market occupied an entire square, and it offered every variety of food and handicraft that could be found in Guatemala. Bundles of firewood were plentiful. Because of the

James Sawders

SELLING FIREWOOD AT THE MARKET

scarcity of coal in Guatemala, many of the people found it necessary to buy wood or charcoal.

Peter and Nancy enjoyed seeing the Indians even more than viewing their products. Their blue-black hair shone in the sunlight, and their skins were like copper. The Indian women in their bright, homespun garments were a picturesque sight. They were merchants in their own right, clever at displaying their wares, and shrewd at selling. Many of these Indians walked a good many miles to sell produce on which there was only a few cents' profit.

Uncle Lee listened smilingly to the children's account of their morning's excursion.

"Do you want to go down to Minerva Park with me this afternoon and see the big relief map of Guatemala?" he asked as the three finished lunch.

Peter and Nancy assented without enthusiasm.

However, they were delighted when they beheld the famous giant relief map inside the race track, a map that covered several acres and revealed every mountain peak, plain, stream, and trail in the whole country of Guatemala.

The afternoon hours flew while Peter and Nancy walked around the map. Uncle Lee became tired, but he realized that the relief map told the geographical story of Guatemala to Peter and Nancy much better than he could tell it. Even the flight in Jimmy's airplane could not give so complete a picture.

Guatemala was, in fact, all mountains and high valleys. The only lowland lay in two strips, along the east and west coasts. Peter counted twenty-eight volcanoes.

"Most of those volcanoes are active." Uncle Lee indicated one with his stick. "That particular volcano erupted in 1902 and covered Quezaltenango with several feet of volcanic ash, and ruined the fine coffee plantations near the town."

While the MacLarens looked on, the water was turned into the relief map, and rivers and lakes began to fill up.

"Now I'll never get you youngsters away!" Uncle Lee looked pleasantly resigned. "Well, that lake there near the Pacific is Lake Atitlán. It's a beautiful blue lake, and it fills the crater of an extinct volcano which is five thousand feet high. The lake itself is apparently bottomless."

"There's another lake!" Nancy exclaimed. "It's very near the capital."

"Lake Amatitlán," Uncle Lee decided. "It's only eighteen miles away. Look at that river. That's the Motagua, near some ruins of the Mayan civilization. We'll visit Quiriguá where other Mayan ruins still stand. Once a city stood there, a glorious city with palaces, cathedrals, and beautiful homes."

As they drove back to the hotel Uncle Lee stopped at the Cerro del Carmen church, an ancient hermitage built in 1620, from which the visitor might gain a fine view of Guatemala City.

On the way to the Mayan ruins at Quiriguá Uncle Lee told Peter and Nancy a great deal about the Mayas. They were, he said, the most highly civilized Indians that ever lived in North America, and they flourished for fifteen hundred years beginning about the time of the birth of Christ. Then they left their beautiful homes and moved northward into Yucatán. The stone cities they left behind have puzzled every scholar who has studied about them.

"Why did they leave their homes, Uncle Lee?" Nancy inquired.

"No one knows," Uncle Lee answered.

"But you must have some idea," Peter urged.

"Earthquakes, possibly," Uncle Lee guessed. "Human enemies who drove them out and then perished of a pestilence themselves. Disease or famine! Almost an impossibility, of course. To me the most likely explanation is that superstition drove them out, perhaps some such superstition as that of the Indians today who believe that demons under the earth want the beautiful lands at the base of the volcanoes for themselves. It may interest you youngsters to know that the ruins of Quiriguá were lost for centuries and were discovered by John Lloyd Stephens, an American, in 1839."

"How could a city be lost?" Peter demanded.

"Vegetation grew up about the buildings," Uncle Lee explained. "Earth formed over them as the rains beat the vegetation down; other plant life made inroads and dirt accumulated."

"Speaking of rains," Nancy put in, "we haven't had a rain since we arrived."

"It's really spring the year round in Guatemala," Uncle Lee announced. "But for practical purposes the natives speak of two seasons, the rainy season from May through October, and the dry season from November through April. Of course, it's the dry season now."

Uncle Lee drove the car between long, green rows of bananas as the MacLarens neared the ruins of Quiriguá.

James Sawders

MAYAN RUINS NEAR QUIRIGUÁ

"The railway company uncovered some of the ruins," Uncle Lee remarked. "But most of the work was done by the United Fruit Company in 1910. This banana plantation, which supplies the company with some of its fruit, covers thirteen thousand acres. Where the bananas grow a Mayan city once stood. About seventy-five acres have been left free from planting. That's where the finest ruins are. Of the seventy-five acres only fifteen have thus far been cleared of jungle growth."

Peter and Nancy gazed in awe at what had once been impressive buildings and monuments. Even in such a state of ruin, with the woodwork decayed and eaten away by ants, the remains were amazing.

"Some of the stones are still buried in the ground, others only partly so," Uncle Lee said, as he pointed out the base of a large stone block.

Peter declared that these stones reminded him of Egypt, for they were covered with hieroglyphics. He did hope that sometime a scholar would find a code similar to the one of the Rosetta stone, that would unlock all the knowledge that remained in the strange writing.

Nancy called out, "There's the queerest face on this stone. It looks like a Chinese face."

"Some scholars think the Mayas may have been Tartars," Uncle Lee answered as he joined Nancy. "That face does look Chinese. The Mayas may have come from Asia after all, cross-

Ewing Galloway

CARVED STONES OF THE MAYAS

ing Bering Strait and journeying down into Central America."

"Here's a turtle that is a turtle!" Peter shouted. "And he's completely covered with hieroglyphics. It would take me a month to read his story, even if I could make out the funny characters."

The turtle that Peter pointed out was fully eight feet high, and Uncle Lee guessed that it weighed at least twenty tons. He went on to tell Peter that the turtle was probably considered sacred by the Mayas just as it was by the Chinese.

"I suppose there are quarries close by," Nancy
volunteered. "That is a pretty big stone to carry
very far."

But Uncle Lee informed her that there were
no quarries near by. There was no natural rock
of any kind. The immense blocks of sandstone
might have been brought down the Motagua
River on rafts, but how such stones were lifted
into place Uncle Lee could not explain. Surely
the Mayas were great builders, perhaps even
greater than the Aztecs.

"I want you to see the banana shipments for
Puerto Barrios, the great east-coast port," Uncle
Lee decided. "I'll make arrangements for us
to stay at the plantation house tonight."

After a good night's rest on the plantation as
guests of the American manager, the MacLarens
were escorted over the plantation in a handcar
pumped by two Negroes, along tracks that ran
for miles between the green plants. Peter had
always wanted to ride on a handcar. Occasionally he was permitted to take one of the handles
and pump it up and down.

Peter and Nancy had seen many banana plantations. They knew that bananas did not grow
on trees but on a great plant having a fleshy
rootstock, known as a rhizome. They knew also
that in this rootstock sprouted large buds or
"eyes"—much like the eyes in potatoes. Pieces
of rootstock had to be planted as one planted a
piece of potato. If the rootstock did not grow,

DELIVERING BANANAS AT A JUNGLE STATION

a shoot of the old plant was stuck into the ground, and it usually grew rapidly in the rich soil. Some children might be surprised on seeing a banana plant. But Peter and Nancy had seen bananas growing before, a single bunch on a plant and hanging just the opposite from the way the grocer hung them at home—seemingly upside-down.

None of the MacLarens ever had seen a ripe banana on a well-run plantation. Bananas were picked when green in order to reach the market a fine yellow color. The fruit was handled very carefully, for if a single banana were bruised the whole bunch would spoil before it reached the market, they were told.

Peter and Nancy found it easy to ask questions in what Uncle Lee called Bananaland. Most of the workers were Negroes, but the managers were either American or English. The Mac-Larens were to hear English spoken all through the Caribbean countries.

"Just when I was beginning to learn Spanish," Peter lamented, as the MacLarens prepared for their next trip.

GLEAMING CITIES AND OLD WELLS

JIMMY Dustin had swooped down out of the dazzling blue sky of Guatemala. Now he was nosing his plane north for a view of the Peninsula of Yucatán. Not all of it, of course, but enough to give Peter and Nancy a glance at the general topography! Jimmy compared the peninsula to the thumb of a giant's hand. Uncle Lee's map had shown that the thumb projected northward from the mainland between the Caribbean Sea and the Gulf of Mexico. Yucatán lay in the northern half with Campeche and Quintana Roo.

A few low foothills appeared on the flat surface of the country. Uncle Lee said that it was really a limestone plain, and Peter worried because there seemed to be no rivers and few lakes.

"Where do people get water?" he inquired.

"There is no surface water to speak of," Uncle Lee answered. "There are many large, natural wells, known as *cenotes*. There's plenty of water in Yucatán, and climatic conditions are good. The nights are always cool, even after the hottest days, because of the trade winds from the Caribbean. But the very hot weather will not begin until April or May."

"Mérida, the capital, is less than nine hours from Miami," Jimmy volunteered. "If you want to pass up Honduras and Nicaragua, Nancy, I can fly you back to your native shores before daybreak."

"I'm glad to know my native shores are so close," Nancy decided, "but I think I'll stay with the rest of you in Yucatán."

The view of Mérida was a startling one.

"Windmills!" Nancy shouted. "Look, Peter! Look, Uncle Lee! Hundreds and hundreds of flat-roofed houses, and enough big windmills so that there must be one for each house. Imagine enough windmills to go around! I must be seeing things!"

And practically every house did possess a well. The wells dated from Spanish times when there were no waterworks. Jimmy said that there were about four thousand windmills and that the trade winds furnished the free power that turned the wheels.

There were, the MacLarens learned, over a hundred thousand people living in Mérida. It was one of the cleanest towns they had visited. Little, flat-roofed houses of rough masonry coated with lime plaster livened the paved streets with their lovely pastel colors of cream, pink, blue, green, and yellow. The yellow houses, of which there seemed to be a great many, were the color of sunshine, Nancy declared.

Jimmy, who had friends in Mérida, took the MacLarens to call at a home whose front, like most of the others, presented grilled windows to

the street. The house was delightful within, and
opened onto a patio blazing with flowers. The
fragrance of the tropical blooms filled the air.
With evening, lights came on all over the city.
Near the MacLarens' hotel electric signs shone
cheerfully. Peter and Nancy boarded an auto-
bus and toured the city, visiting the parks and
returning in time to see a movie. A bootblack
with a portable box shined Peter's shoes for a few
cents, and a sweetmeat vender persuaded Nancy
to buy some of his candied cactus.

The crowds were a strange mixture, the Mexicans dressed in modern garb, the Mayan Indians
in picturesque native costumes, and tourists in
conventional American clothes. The cathedral,
located on the east side of the central plaza, looked
down upon the oddly assorted peoples and upon
the numerous windmills that so intrigued Nancy.

Uncle Lee explained that the earliest history
of Yucatán was to be found in its caves. These
cave dwellers, he said, may have been the ancestors of the Mayas who built the cities of cut
stones. Both used the same utensils, the same
kind of water jars, the same corn grinders, and
even the same kind of jade ornaments, earplugs,
beads, and pendants. The excavations were right
there in Yucatán to tell the story of the Mayan
civilization.

Sitting on a bench in a plaza near the hotel,
Uncle Lee made a startling statement: "Mayan
civilization was founded on corn!"

"On corn!" Peter and Nancy shouted it together, and Nancy added, "We've eaten tortillas at almost every meal since we left home, and the sound of corn cakes being patted into shape is the most common sound we've heard. But to say corn means culture is a different matter. Now, isn't it?"

Uncle Lee, however, had the most plausible explanation. The Mayas were farmers, and as such they were interested in the different seasons of the year: when the corn should be planted, when it should be harvested, and when the dried leaves should be burned. To measure time the priests began the study of astronomy. They invented a chronology, or calendar, exact to the day within a period of 37,000 years.

"Maybe you won't understand how important my next statement is," Uncle Lee challenged the two interested children. "But the Mayas were among the first people in human history to use the symbol zero. Now don't laugh! For the first time numbers were placed by position, but no one had thought of zero as a symbol for the point of reckoning. You'll understand better when you're older. These Mayan priests had accurate knowledge of the heavenly bodies, could foretell eclipses, and could determine the length of a year. How important that was, you will see."

"They had a regular weather bureau, I suppose," Peter suggested. "The priests were the weather men."

James Sawders

THE GREAT CALENDAR STONE OF THE AZTECS

"Exactly." To Peter's surprise, Uncle Lee agreed. "The wealth of the Mayas was in corn. They were agriculturists, and as such were interested in the weather."

"Farmers like us!" Nancy put in. "Only, in their case, corn was the staff of life instead of wheat bread."

"Good!" said Uncle Lee. "Knowledge of the seasons enabled the Mayas to grow more corn. Then they knew when to plant. More corn, more wealth! More wealth, more leisure! More lei-

Ewing Galloway

THE TEMPLE AT UXMAL

sure, more attention to such things as art, sculpture, architecture, ceramics, and featherwork,
too! Some of the headdresses of the chiefs must
have been magnificent."

As Uncle Lee talked, Peter and Nancy could
almost see the cities of the fourth to eighth centuries. He pictured great public buildings made
of stone and decorated with brilliantly painted
stucco. He described tall pyramids on top of
which stood temples towering to the sky—the
first skyscrapers in America.

Then there were the monasteries and palaces and observatories; there were even stone courts where ball was played. As in modern Indian villages, these stone cities had a central plaza, but they also had very high terraces. Monuments of from five to twenty-five feet in height graced these terraces as well as the plazas. The monuments were erected at ten-year intervals to commemorate events or to make calendar corrections.

During the eighth century the building ceased. The priests began moving northward into Yucatán, and the common people withdrew from the cities and let the jaguar and the deer roam their grass-grown streets.

"Once," said Uncle Lee, "I gave you a number of rather dramatic reasons why the Mayas left their cities of stone: earthquakes, enemies, or epidemics. Now I want you to know what our own agriculturists think. They have an explanation that will appear very reasonable to you youngsters who have been brought up on an American farm. They think the land wore out."

"I know!" Peter was eager. "Our Department of Agriculture found out that the second-year crop from a field is only about two-thirds as large as the first year's crop. The third year's crop will be a third less than the second year's. The Mayan fields simply wore out, that was all."

"Good reasoning, Peter!" Uncle Lee approved. "Even today the Mexicans find it easier to clear a new patch than to fight the weeds in an old corn patch. The new patch means burning trees. In Mayan times the forests were burned, the corn was planted, and eventually there were no more forests to clear. Grass grew over the land. The Mayan with his stone ax and his wooden planting stick was unable to cope with his problem. Mayan agricultural life had come to an end."

On the way back to town Uncle Lee said, "I wish that we had time to visit a chicle camp so that you might see the natives preparing some of the material used in chewing gum. But that will be impossible now. The trip would require several days, and we must leave tomorrow."

Then Uncle Lee explained: "Chicle is usually found in dense jungle. To obtain the material, gashes are cut in the tree, one below the other, so that the sap can flow down to the bottom of the tree. The sap is taken to the camp where it is boiled until it stiffens like sugar syrup. It is then poured and molded. A block of molded chicle is worth from five to ten dollars. The shipment of the blocks is very difficult in the rainy season, because four or more days are required to transport it from the camp to the railroad station."

That afternoon, Jimmy flew the MacLarens to Chichen Itzá, one of the stone cities, to show them more ruins of the Mayan civilization. Soaring above the ruins of stone pyramids and temples, Peter and Nancy thrilled to the story the

CUTTING TREES FOR CHICLE

A BLOCK OF MOLDED CHICLE

excavations told, the story of a lost civilization.

"Chichen Itzá," Uncle Lee said, "meant, in the Mayan language, 'the mouths of the wells of Itzá.' "

Uncle Lee located the two wells for which the city had been named. Cenote de Xtoloc, or the lizard well, in the center of the city, had two masonry stairways down its deep sides. This well had supplied the city with water. The other, Cenote Sagrado, at the eastern end of the city, was known as the well of sacrifice. Into this well young maidens had been hurled at dawn to appease angry gods who were visiting the people with droughts or famine. The Itzá people also flung their worldly possessions into this well.

Uncle Lee said the Carnegie Institution at Washington had retrieved such valuables as jade earplugs, nose rings, gold beads and rings, carved bones, shells, and carved wooden weapons.

One of the most elaborate buildings to be restored and reclaimed by the Carnegie scientists was the Temple of the Warriors. It stood there in the bright sunlight, gleaming white, a pyramid-sanctuary and colonnade. On its pillars were many sculptures of fighting men, no two alike.

Peter strove to identify men, jaguars, and monkeys on the panels, but Uncle Lee said that it took an archeologist to explain the carvings.

El Castillo was a very large temple which rose seventy-five feet in the air and was approached by staircases on all four sides. Its serpent-pillars were of a kind known in few other places.

Feathered serpents were plentiful in the decorations. In fact, the two high columns that guarded the entrance to the Temple of the Warriors represented feathered serpents. Uncle Lee pointed out the fact that the heads with their wide-open mouths lay on the ground. The body formed the column, and the tail with tufts of feathers rose above it. Before the entrance lay a strange stone figure holding a plate for offerings. Jimmy pointed out some of the soldiers carved in relief.

Ewing Galloway

EL CASTILLO AND ITS STAIRCASES

"Once," he said, "they were very lifelike. Their eyes were made of white shell with small circles of black pitch to form the pupils. The relief was usually painted in bright colors."

On the tops of some of the temples were superstructures that looked like tall walls. They had, Uncle Lee said, purely a decorative purpose. He pointed out one that had, he insisted, figures of rulers in it, but to Peter it was just a stone wall through the crevices of which cacti grew.

The MacLarens knew that one visit to Chichen Itzá would not be enough, nor would a dozen visits be. It would still have much to offer.

Ewing Galloway
HAULING BALES OF HENEQUEN FIBER

On the way back Peter asked to stop at a hacienda where henequen fiber was being baled. This golden fiber was made from a plant which the MacLarens had seen growing close by. Nancy said each plant looked like a bunch of sharp spurs, but she knew that sisal was a great source of wealth in Yucatán.

The henequen was being loaded on a truck to be taken to Progreso, the port of Yucatán. From Progreso it would be shipped to New Orleans.

"And from New Orleans it will, in time, reach Minnesota as binder twine," Peter prophesied.

TO THE CITY OF SILVER HILLS

JIMMY Dustin's plane had left Yucatán and now it was zooming above Honduras, just east of the Guatemalan border. Like Guatemala, Uncle Lee said, Honduras had only a strip of swamp land on either coast but plenty of high plateaus and mountains back from the coast.

"Down there," Jimmy shouted, "is the cordillera, or main range of mountains. It runs northwest-southeast, and is parallel to the Pacific. We're above it now, which means that we're flying about fifty miles inland from the coast."

The earliest explorers had discovered pyramids and carved stones in Honduras. These adventurers had been seeking gold and silver. Did they discover what they sought? Nancy wanted to know. Jimmy said that they certainly did— silver particularly. He had visited the American-owned mines of Rosario at San Juancito, just twenty-five miles from the capital. These mines, he said, were the largest in Central America and attracted much more attention than did the pyramids and the carved stones.

"Honduras in Spanish means 'great depths,'" Uncle Lee put in. "Columbus gave it that name because he had difficulty in anchoring his boats in the deep water along the Atlantic coast."

"Great Depths is a good name for the inte-

194

rior, too," Peter declared. "Jimmy would have a hard time anchoring his ship on one of these mountainsides. That field down there is certainly on the upgrade. You could slide down the field with a sickle in your hand and cut corn."

The pine and oak forests were rich and beautiful. Here and there rubber trees and coconut groves appeared, especially when Jimmy swung downward toward the coast. There were bananas, too, though Jimmy said the great banana plantations were on the north coast. Once in a while a few cattle were visible, and often a mule appeared carrying a load along a trail. But nowhere did there seem to be any great center of population.

"I thought that Guatemala had few people," Nancy observed, "but Honduras seems even less populous. Good word, Peter—populous!"

"Honduras has only a third as many people as Guatemala," Uncle Lee informed Nancy. "Most of them are of Indian and Spanish descent. On the north coast where the big banana plantations thrive there are plenty of Negroes. And on the Mosquito Coast you'll find Caribs."

"Caribs!" Peter cried. "I'd like to see some Caribs. Once they inhabited these coastlands and were such terrors that they gave the name to the Caribbean Sea. If a runaway slave escaped from the islands to the Mosquito Coast, he had a sure refuge. At least, it took a daring soul to go after him."

"Caribs today are not what they were," Uncle Lee remarked dryly. "But Honduras hasn't changed much. You youngsters may be glad Jimmy is flying us to Tegucigalpa. I believe it's the only capital on the American continent that has no railway."

"Asunción in Paraguay has none," Peter said. "But of course that's in South America."

"Aren't there any railways in Honduras?" Nancy inquired.

"There is a government railway that runs toward the capital from Puerto Cortés on the north coast," Uncle Lee answered. "But it gets discouraged and stops at a little town in the foothills. An automobile may get you along some of the trails, but mules are the safest means of travel. There are few hotels. A native might let you hang a hammock in his windowless house."

"Do the people of Honduras sleep in hammocks?" Nancy inquired.

"No," Jimmy answered that question. "They have no beds of any kind as a rule, and there are no floors in their houses. They are not needed. It's a grand climate. They sleep on sun-dried oxhides on the ground. For blankets they use empty grain sacks. There are always plenty of beans to eat and the usual tortillas—a trifle heavy, perhaps. If you like your coffee black, you'll be happy here. The women have their own way of cooking eggs. They always break a little hole in an egg before they boil it."

Ewing Galloway

A JUNGLE IN HONDURAS

"Why a hole in it?" Nancy inquired. "I usually make a hole in mine afterward."

"They think," Jimmy explained, "there must be a hole so the boiling water can get inside the egg."

Jimmy was flying as low as he dared above the forests and plunging mountain streams where an occasional bright-leaved mahogany tree rose above the dark green of the pines. Such trees, Jimmy told them, were worth about ten thousand dollars, but it was difficult to get them to market.

"The natives make fence posts and furniture of such wood," Jimmy declared. "Imagine solid mahogany fence posts!"

The engine settled to a steady hum.

"We're directly over the Royal Highway!" Jimmy announced after awhile. He turned around to grin mischievously at Peter and Nancy. "In Spanish it would be called *El Camino Real.*"

"Where is it?" Nancy shouted, and Peter echoed, "Where?"

The two MacLaren children saw only the green jungle, a patch of corn on a hillside, fenced with mahogany if Jimmy were right, and a stony brook near a grassy path. There was no sign of human life, but there were a number of crooked telegraph poles with a lone, sagging wire strung on them.

"The telegraph lines belong to the government," Uncle Lee said. "You can send a message anywhere in Honduras for a nickel."

"Please let's get back to that Royal Highway,"

Nancy begged. "Point it out before we leave it."

"There's no hurry," Jimmy said calmly. "It goes all the way to Tegucigalpa from the Guatemalan border. For all its splendid name, it's nothing more than a trail. It goes up hill and down dale. Once in awhile it climbs a few stone steps, and it may even turn into a fairly good road for a short distance. It's not at all easy to follow, though the telegraph lines do help."

Jimmy's explanation was interrupted by an exclamation from Peter.

"A town! A town!" he shouted.

The town below was Santa Rosa, a pretty little place with a white church. Jimmy said that there were no electric lights or automobiles in Santa Rosa, but as he saluted the town, Peter and Nancy caught a glimpse of cobblestone streets.

Then the plane zoomed on, gaining altitude. Another city appeared below. It was Comayagua, Jimmy said, the second largest town in Honduras. He pointed out a sheep pasture which also served as a plaza in the middle of the town. This slow little town—at least it appeared lazy in the sunlight—had once been the capital of Honduras.

"Tegucigalpa will probably be much better," Nancy decided. "A city called the 'City of Silver Hills' would have to be romantic."

"Names don't mean a thing here," Peter teased. "Your Silver Hills may be on a par with the Royal Highway."

The first view of Tegucigalpa showed a town hedged in by mountains across which the setting sun threw exquisite light and color. Over the hills wound two roads that looked like tan ribbons. A whitewashed cathedral with twin towers dominated the town and looked down on the one-story buildings with their red tile roofs.

With some difficulty Jimmy brought the plane down in an open field not far from the town, and the four adventurers walked along the pathway on Picacho, a hill that overlooked the capital.

The central plaza, in which the MacLaren party eventually found itself, was not particularly lively. There was an arbor covered with purple bougainvillea and there were concrete walks, but Peter and Nancy were more interested in food and sleep than in purple flowers.

The bare rooms of the hotel looked inviting, even though the beds proved to be cots that sagged from long usage.

Breakfast next morning consisted of oranges, boiled eggs, tortillas, and black coffee. The servants were barefoot, and no one seemed to mind the dogs and chickens that wandered in to pick up scraps of food.

The fresh mountain air was like a tonic, and the little shops were pleasant places in which to wander about.

After a two days' rest Jimmy flew his friends down to the coast on the Gulf of Fonseca, where Uncle Lee, Peter, and Nancy boarded a launch for

Amapala, on an island twenty-four miles off the coast.

After finding a comfortable hotel in Amapala Uncle Lee decided on an excursion. Early next morning he secured horses, and the three Mac-Larens rode to the top of an extinct volcano on the island.

"From this point," Uncle Lee explained as he drew rein, "we can see three countries. Off there is Honduras! There is Salvador! And there is Nicaragua! Tomorrow we'll start out to visit the neighbors again!"

TWO LITTLE COUNTRIES AND A BIG ONE

THE MacLarens landed on the coast of Salvador in the same launch that had taken them over to Amapala. From the ocean they could see that Salvador was not lowland. From the coast rose a low plain that mounted to a level plateau from which cone-shaped mountains poked up into the bright sky. Nancy counted a number of them and Peter asked, "Volcanoes?"

"They're the shape of volcanoes, anyway, Peter," Nancy decided.

"They're volcanoes, all right," Uncle Lee agreed. "One of them—Izalco—has been erupting for over a hundred years. It lights up the sky nightly, and sailors call it the 'Lighthouse of Salvador.' Salvador is like Guatemala in respect to volcanoes. In other respects, it's quite different."

"For example?" prompted Peter.

"It's much smaller, about the size of a big banana plantation or a cattle range—140 miles long and 60 miles wide. But it is thickly populated. There are more inhabitants here than in any other country in Central America. To be exact, there are more than a million people living in thirteen thousand square miles of territory, which makes Salvador one of the most crowded countries in the world. The Black Republic of Haiti in the West Indies is the only country in the western hemisphere more thickly populated."

The next day Jimmy arrived and the Mac-Larens were soon soaring above the busy little country that Jimmy pronounced one of the most industrious in the world.

"When there are so many people living close together," he explained, "everyone has to work harder to make a living. Look down below!"

The hills over which the plane flew were cultivated to the very tops. There were little patches of corn here such as Peter and Nancy had seen in Honduras and Guatemala. Every acre of space was being utilized. It was a delight to look down into the cultivated valleys even though there was less forest to enjoy than in Honduras.

The land seemed to be divided into little farms, and there were no large estates as in Guatemala, with the native people working for a foreign owner. Each man owned his own land, acres made fertile by volcanic ash. Jimmy pointed out Mount San Miguel, which was smoking. The children looked down on several rivers flowing toward the Pacific. They watered land planted with corn and coffee.

"A school teacher from Brazil started the coffee industry here in 1840," Jimmy informed the Mac-Larens. "He planted a coffee tree in his garden, and they say these trees are the descendants."

"A large percentage of Salvador's exports is coffee," Uncle Lee put in. "France and Germany use most of it. Indigo is important, too, and there are some minerals here, including silver and gold. It's a great little country."

"Look at that grove of willows!" Nancy pointed out. "It seems odd to see so many together. At home we have only a hedge near the pond."

"That's indigo," Uncle Lee explained, laughing. "Those branches that look like willow switches are soaked in water to which chemicals have been added in order to extract the indigo. Then the mixture is boiled down to a paste."

"We may get our bluing from Salvador for all we know," Nancy decided. "And this blue suit may have been dyed with switches from that very farm. I like the idea."

Then Jimmy announced that he was going to fly over the city of San Salvador.

"And don't confuse this San Salvador with the little island in the West Indies where Columbus landed," he warned. "After I've shown you San Salvador in its perfect setting, you'll never forget it. I think it's the most beautiful city in Central America."

Jimmy had not exaggerated. San Salvador lay on a green plateau among green hills at the base of a volcanic mountain. Deep ravines had been worn by mountain streams, a protection against enemies and a benefit for land that was never thirsty. In the city a cathedral pointed to the sky, and government buildings presented handsome facades to the central plaza. The wide, cobbled streets were straight, as though the city

James Sawders

THE CRATER OF COSEGÜINA VOLCANO

had been carefully planned, and the sidewalks were of stone and cement. The thick-walled houses had lovely, flowery patios, just as the city itself had beautiful plazas with palm trees and flowers.

"In spite of earthquakes San Salvador has never become discouraged," Uncle Lee observed. "It is modern and progressive. It has good water, good schools, and a good telegraph system. It has even a good public health department."

Regretfully the MacLarens took leave of Salvador. The same launch returned them to Amapala in Honduras. From Amapala they sailed by steamer to Corinto, the chief Pacific port of Nicaragua.

As the steamer passed Cosegüina Point, they sighted the extinct volcano Cosegüina. Uncle Lee told Peter and Nancy that in 1835 this volcano burned out completely, blowing up to such an extent that ashes were carried as far north as New Orleans, Louisiana and south to Lima, Peru. Only the crater remains today.

There was no time to visit British Honduras. Uncle Lee said it was a low country bordering on the Caribbean and that it shipped mahogany, chicle, tortoise shell, and sponges. He pointed out its location on his map, to the east of Guatemala and the peninsula of Yucatán.

At Corinto the MacLarens boarded a train and rode thirty-five miles to León, the largest city in Nicaragua.

In exploring the city, they found the streets and houses picturesquely Spanish. Most of the houses were made of adobe and many had fine gardens. Important events in the history of Nicaragua were re-enacted in the imaginations of Peter and Nancy as they visited the famous historic buildings of the city: the Church of the Recollection, the palace of the bishop, the fortified barracks built originally as a Franciscan monastery, and the university.

From León the MacLarens went by rail to

James Sawders

THE CHURCH OF THE RECOLLECTION

Managua, the capital of Nicaragua. Uncle Lee informed Peter and Nancy that this railway, which was only 175 miles long, was the only government-owned railway in Nicaragua.

"And Nicaragua is the largest country in Central America," Uncle Lee said. "It has nearly fifty thousand square miles! Although it extends from ocean to ocean, the people live in the western third of the country, the highest, most healthful part. You'll notice that all the cities are on the Pacific slope, where most of Nicaragua's 750,000 people live."

Peter and Nancy were disappointed in Managua. It was a city of narrow, cobbled streets. The little houses were one-storied, tinted in gay colors, and roofed with red tile. But the colors were dingy with dust, and although the city was located on the southern shore of Lake Managua, the air was hot and sticky. Dust covered everything from the central plaza to the side streets. It sifted into homes and public buildings alike, obliterating the colors of plaster and tiles. Even the imposing old cathedral faced a barren expanse of sand.

"We can expect it to be hot," Uncle Lee grumbled, "in a town only a little over a hundred feet above sea level!"

At the hotel Uncle Lee visited with the proprietor who boasted of his country's future. He spoke of mahogany, rosewood, logwood, and sandalwood in the forests. He said there were limitless supplies of gums, dyes, and medicinal herbs. Nicaragua grew fine corn. It produced the best coffee, the finest sugar, and the largest bananas in Central America. It raised beef cattle that were the envy of the Argentine. Peter and Nancy laughed heartily with the innkeeper as he talked, and they decided that this Nicaraguan was both enthusiastic and progressive.

Uncle Lee took Peter and Nancy on a horseback trip to view Lake Nicaragua, among the largest bodies of fresh water in the world. It was, Uncle Lee said, 115 miles long.

"Once Nicaragua was considered a better location than Panama for a canal between the Atlantic and the Pacific Oceans," Uncle Lee said. "Lake Nicaragua is 110 feet above sea level. It drains into the Caribbean Sea through the San Juan River. The mountain range is quite low between the lake and the ocean. If the San Juan River were dredged, ocean steamers could come up to the lake. Then from the lake a canal could be dug, a canal only eleven miles long, that would enable boats to pass into the Pacific."

"And will it be built?" Peter inquired.

"Yes, I think so," Uncle Lee answered. "If the traffic through the Panama Canal becomes too great, it will be built.

"The air lines are doing a great deal for this country," he went on to say. "No longer does Central America seem just a name. Jimmy says the landing field here is very good.

"But good night, now, or we shall not be ready for him in the morning."

A RICH COAST AND COUNTRY

JIMMY Dustin's seaplane had been hovering over the placid blue Caribbean for an hour or more.

"Mosquito Coast down below!" he announced. "And don't ask me if it was named after that pest, the mosquito."

"We know better," Peter boasted. "It got its name from the Miskitos or Mosquitoes, a race of mixed African and Indian blood."

"What's that town, Jimmy?" asked Nancy.

"Greytown, or San Juan del Norte," Jimmy answered, circling lower. "It may be the Caribbean terminus of the Nicaraguan Canal some day."

Greytown lay on a low, swampy shore, a small, unattractive town whose citizens, Uncle Lee said, were mostly black.

The plane saluted, soared aloft, and finally came down in the harbor of Port Limón. The children had a brief view of a crescent-shaped beach whose white sand was fringed with graceful coconut palms. Then Jimmy made a fine landing.

"At Limón, here," Uncle Lee announced, as he climbed out of the cockpit and reached up for the luggage Peter was handing down, "we can take a train to San José, the capital. Limón happens to be the eastern terminus of the transcontinental railway. It sounds much longer than it actually is. Come on, Nancy. Jump!"

Peter scanned the coast, with the blue water washing up on the white sand. It looked like any ordinary tropical seacoast.

"Why is it called the Rich Coast?" he inquired. "Costa Rica means 'rich coast,' doesn't it?"

"It furnishes turtle soup, Peter," Uncle Lee said solemnly. "And it gives Nancy tortoise-shell combs, and tortoise-shell jewelry. If she wants pink pearls, though, she'll have to look for them on the Pacific side."

"How about something practical?" Peter demanded.

"Bananas and coffee," Jimmy put in. "More bananas and more coffee on the Rich Coast, bananas near the sea and coffee in the hills! You'll find tobacco growing and cacao and rubber trees and vanilla beans. And you'll see cattle; many hides are exported. But in the end, Peter, you'll always have a vision of Costa Rica as a land of bananas and coffee."

Uncle Lee said that the Negro people Peter and Nancy saw in such great numbers on the streets of Limón were not true Costa Ricans. They were British West Indians brought over from Jamaica to work on the plantations.

Jimmy's prophecy proved true. From the moment the train pulled out of the port with its square blocks and well-paved streets, until it

Ewing Galloway

COFFEE TREES ON A PLANTATION

reached San José, the scenery was enchanting. Peter and Nancy in a comfortable parlor car with wide windows began to enjoy the changing panorama of banana plantations, fields of sugar cane, dense forests of magnificent trees, and little thatched villages. Up, up, up climbed the train, leaving behind the blue rivers of the valleys and shunting around winding cliffs that rose above palm trees.

Now there were no more banana lands, but up on the cool, steep hillsides grew coffee trees, the red berries shining in the sun. Uncle Lee said most of this excellent Costa Rican coffee was sold in European countries.

The air was fresh and bracing. It was not surprising to learn that Costa Rica's mountains spelled vacation land for many a traveler or Canal Zone employee. The MacLarens realized that Costa Rica was mountainous everywhere but on the east coast. They saw several volcanic peaks, but Uncle Lee said that nearly all of the little country's twenty-three thousand square miles was safe from eruptions. Between the mountains there were lovely valleys with fine spots of level farmland.

As the train reached the summit, Uncle Lee pointed out a mountain peak from which both the Atlantic and Pacific oceans could be seen.

The train began to descend; Uncle Lee said it went down two thousand feet on its way to the capital. It stopped at Cartago, the old capital, a town of red-tiled roofs lying on the slope of the volcano Irazu. It was such a gay, sunny little city that Peter and Nancy could hardly realize that back in April, 1910, a tenth of the population had perished in a terrific earthquake that shook the city.

The train puffed into a fertile valley, running between small farms, and stopped at a station from which could be seen green-velvet mountains enclosing a city, the city of San José.

An hour later, the MacLarens came out of a

modern hotel onto a delightfully quaint street scene. Above the little one- and two-story Spanish houses rose the majestic cathedral; and through the narrow streets plodded many teams of oxen, their noses almost touching the ground, their heavy shoulders swinging from side to side. As in Mexico the yoke was bound to the horns, but here in San José the driver walked ahead, turning back to goad the animals in their necks, if they were too slow.

Nancy was most interested in the women, for nearly every one was as handsome as an artist's portrait of a Spanish beauty, and nearly every one wore a large silk shawl, elaborately embroidered and having a long, rich fringe. Even the poorest women going about barefoot wore shawls of rich fabric and gleaming colors.

On a horseback ride into the country with Uncle Lee, Peter and Nancy saw the Costa Ricans at work among the coffee trees. They seemed to be the busiest, happiest people they had seen in Central America.

"Costa Rica was settled by people from Galicia in northwestern Spain, hard-working farmers who loved peace and plenty," Uncle Lee explained. "Eighty per cent of these people are pure Spanish. Salvador and Costa Rica may be the two smallest republics on the American continent, but they are also the most progressive."

As the three riders returned to San José, Uncle Lee told Peter and Nancy of the fine

Costa Rican people. They had refused to join
the other Central American countries in a fed-
eration because they knew they could get along
better by themselves. They did not care, for
instance, to be embroiled in Nicaragua's frequent
revolutions.

"Five-sixths of Costa Rica is still forest and
jungle," Uncle Lee declared. "The four big cities
of the country are all connected by this wagon
road on which we are riding, and it's only about
thirty miles long."

Back in San José the MacLarens spent a day
resting and making plans for the trip to Panama.

OLD GLORY IN PANAMA

THE MacLarens were enjoying themselves in Jimmy Dustin's seaplane. To them it was quite as wonderful as the Clipper Ship that some of their tourist friends had taken in Salvador.

"We can't very well leave Central America without seeing Panama," Peter declared. "After all, Panama is one of the most important countries in Central America."

"Not only because of its canal," Nancy added, "but because the Stars and Stripes fly over the Panama Canal Zone."

"You're not very good navigators," Jimmy teased. "If you were, you'd realize that I'm Panama bound right now. That water below is the Pacific. If you insist on seeing a little country smaller than the state of Indiana, it's all right with me. Uncle Lee is certainly indulgent. You've been through the canal before—when you visited South America."

"Look below!" Uncle Lee shouted. "There's a steamer bound for San Francisco. That should help you youngsters to orient yourselves."

The dry Pacific coast, in startling contrast to the tropical vegetation they had left behind, gave way to the blue water of the Gulf of Panama. The plane came to rest in the port of Balboa, at the Pacific end of the canal.

"Old Glory!" Peter shouted, as the plane floated in to shore, towed by a launch. "There it is, flying over the public buildings and the warehouses as well!"

"Ancón Hill!" Uncle Lee pointed upward. "Our flag floats over the hospital there. The great hotels take pride in displaying it, too."

To the east lay the city of Panama, the capital of the Panama republic.

"We'll spend a day in the city," Uncle Lee promised. "The great canal is right at its front porch, you might say."

"Then we'll climb up and over into the Caribbean Sea," Peter added. "Uncle Lee, may we go to the old Central Hotel? I'd like to see a room where the miners stored their sacks of gold back in 1849. It would have been exciting to live here then, in the days of pirates."

Late that afternoon, after depositing their luggage at an hotel, the MacLaren party went over to Central Park, or Independence Square, to watch the colorful crowds of Panama City and to listen to the band. Peter readily recognized Hindus with white-turbaned heads, and Nancy pointed out slant-eyed Orientals in loose black coats and wide pantaloons. Jimmy said that the kinky-headed Negroes with the gleaming smiles were probably descendants of the Cimarron slaves. Their ancestors, he declared, were brought over from Africa long ago by the Spaniards, to be sold as slaves. But the ships in which these

Negroes were prisoners were wrecked, and the Cimarrons escaped into the jungle. Less exciting was the story of the Jamaica Negroes who came from their island to live in the fertile jungle where clothes were not needed and food was plentiful.

"That man isn't a Negro." Nancy indicated a tall, bronze figure in a queer, loose skirt. "He looks like an Indian."

"Good guess!" Jimmy agreed. "He happens to be dressed in the modern way. Most of the Indians near Darien Bay go about in loin cloths made of animal skins."

"Like Tarzan of the Apes," Peter supplied.

"Almost," Jimmy agreed. "I wish we might be poled up the Turia River in a *piragua* or dugout canoe. Nancy could sit under the roof of the little hut that is always built in the middle of the boat, and she would see tall coconut palms, giant ferns, and wild animals. The Indians make pets of the sloths often, but they kill the giant lizards or iguanas for the meat in their tails.

"There are little villages up there where the houses are built on stilts ten feet high," Jimmy continued. "The stilts keep the wild animals from coming too close in dry weather and keep floods from deluging the house in the wet season. It's not very pleasant to have some wild animal use your bedroom for a lair!"

"Let's walk down to the bay and take a look at the boats," Uncle Lee suggested.

THE IGUANA OR GIANT LIZARD

The bay of Panama was full of sailboats bobbing about like corks on the choppy waves. The natives, who Uncle Lee said were half-breeds, were busy unloading produce from their own particular boats. Bananas, coconuts, pawpaws, and dried nuts began to form great piles on the wharves beside live chickens and squealing pigs. Good-natured laughter rose on all sides.

"Some of those fellows," Jimmy guessed, "may have come down from as far as the Chucunaque River. It's a very rough and tumble sort of river, and the village of El Real up there is a decidedly primitive town. It's built on a small peninsula and is the oldest settlement on the Pacific side of the mountains. It is a nice clean little village where the main street is edged with grass huts."

"I'd like to see the huts," Nancy decided.

"They're beautifully made," Jimmy informed her. "The women lace the leaves of the fan palm together to make remarkable roofs. The knots are all on the inside of the hut. The cracks are filled with grasses. The outside of one of those huts is smooth and waterproof, and you'd be surprised how cool it is on the inside. Those primitive people have their own system of insulation and air conditioning."

A long walk about Panama revealed nothing of the city's early life except the old walls that once had helped to protect the citizens from the pirates who threatened their peace. Along paved streets where the clang of the streetcars was common, the city was ablaze with electric lights at dusk. Among the many fine public buildings, which included the university, none was so attractive to Peter and Nancy as the old Cathedral of San José with its twin towers.

"Do you want to see the golden altar?" Uncle Lee asked and led his eager companions into the quiet church.

There were fine old mural paintings on the walls, but the eyes of Peter and Nancy were fixed upon the golden altar that shone like sunlight. Uncle Lee had already told them of the altar's history, also of another of Panama's most valuable relics, a solid gold cross. When Morgan, the pirate, had come to destroy the town, the faithful church people had put out to sea. There they stayed several weeks, returning to find the town in ashes and the survivors starting a new city five miles from the old one. The altar and cross had been painted white so as not to attract the pirates. They remained painted until 1904 when the Panama Canal Zone came under American control.

Jimmy returned to Balboa and his plane, but the MacLarens went through the great Panama Canal by boat. They left Balboa early in the morning on a fine, large passenger steamer.

"Only fifty miles from the deep water of the Pacific Ocean to the deep water of the Atlantic!" Uncle Lee marveled as the three took their places in their deck chairs and prepared to enjoy the trip. "Nor does it seem possible that until August, 1914, this little strip of land connecting North and South America should have blocked the commerce of the world."

Peter and Nancy, squinting into the bright sunlight, begged Uncle Lee to refresh their memories with the story of the building of the great canal. Uncle Lee needed no encouragement. He was very proud of his country's part in the history of Panama. As Nancy said, one could almost see the Stars and Stripes waving as Uncle Lee talked.

Uncle Lee began his story with the account

of how the great Ferdinand de Lesseps, the man who had dug the Suez Canal, undertook the project. He seemed the best qualified man in the world for such a task. But digging a canal through flat desert land and digging a canal through a stubborn mountain range were widely different jobs. The French government, however, spent several million dollars before becoming discouraged. Finally a new French company sold its right to build the canal to the United States for forty million dollars.

"Then things began to happen," Peter put in. "Colombia wouldn't agree to our building the canal. Panama declared its independence, and, by treaty with Panama, we acquired our ten-mile strip called the Canal Zone."

"And we dug the canal right through the middle of it," Nancy continued. "Because our engineers knew a sea-level canal wouldn't do, they built a lock canal. It is like going up and down a water stairway."

"Remember," Uncle Lee reminded Peter and Nancy, "that it required many millions of dollars to build this canal. Remember, too, what an undertaking it was, cutting down and blasting out the earth and rock of the Gaillard Cut through the mountains, and damming the Chagres River. The famous dam, as you already know, is the Gatun Dam, and the lake is Gatun Lake. The water of Gatun Lake flows through the pass and fills the locks so that the ships may

Ewing Galloway

THE PEDRO MIGUEL LOCKS OF THE PANAMA CANAL

be raised and lowered. Do you know the engineer who did the planning?"

"Goethals!" Peter shouted.

"George Washington Goethals!" Nancy added. She got to her feet.

"Look!" she cried. "There's a guide drawing up a bucket of water from the side of the ship. I suppose those tourists want to taste it. Come on, Peter!"

The guide was explaining to his party of Americans that they were about to cross a great fresh-water bridge. He begged them to taste the water in the bucket and even passed out some little paper cups. Peter and Nancy grinned at each other like world-old travelers, but they tasted the water with the rest. It was salty and bitter.

"Wait till we get to Miraflores!" the guide prophesied. "There you will find clear, pure water from the mountains!"

Later on that day the ship was raised to fresh, crystal-clear Lake Miraflores and passed through eight-mile-long Gaillard Cut. Then after traversing the twenty-four miles of Gatun Lake the vessel dropped down through the Gatun Locks and headed for the salty Atlantic.

"Only seven miles from Gatun Locks to the ocean!" Peter exulted. "We'll soon be in Cristobal, our Atlantic port. I hope Jimmy will be there."

ODD WAYS IN THE CARIBBEAN

"THE West Indies! There's a misnomer for you," Jimmy Dustin observed as he warmed up his motor on the beach at Cristobal before taking off. He glanced back at the MacLarens in the cockpit and grinned. "As every school child knows, Christopher Columbus thought he had reached India when he landed on San Salvador. But what every school child does not know is that in the Caribbean—especially in the Virgin Islands, owned by Uncle Sam—bluefish are red, cherries grow on bushes, and gooseberries are found on trees."

"Yes?" Nancy raised an eyebrow, suspiciously.

"Certainly. I've been there," Uncle Lee put in. "Breakfast invariably means lunch, and people say good evening in the afternoon."

"Oh, you two!" Nancy scoffed. "You can't tell me that a little geographical distance would make such a difference. Why, the West Indies lie between Florida on the north, Yucatán on the west, and the coast of South America on the south. The trade routes are quite familiar. I never heard such stories."

"You'll hear a great deal more of the West Indies in the future." Uncle Lee was more serious now. "The building of the Panama Canal, the development of South America, and the new knowledge of tropical products are all going to make the West Indies important to commerce. Since the United States and Great Britain own many of the islands, there should be a fine friendship between the English-speaking peoples in the Caribbean."

"Port-of-Spain is our first call," Jimmy announced as he took off.

Uncle Lee reached over and laid a folder down before Peter and Nancy who sat side by side.

"Glance that over!" he suggested. "It's a fine map of the West Indies. There's Cuba and Jamaica, Hispaniola, and Puerto Rico, which form the Greater Antilles. That group of smaller islands, stretching from Puerto Rico to the mainland of South America, make up the Lesser Antilles. Jamaica belongs to the British. As you know, Cuba is independent. So is Hispaniola."

"And Puerto Rico belongs to us," Nancy added.

The plane droned on above a green sea along the north coast of South America, coming down at Port-of-Spain for refueling, only to take off for Martinique.

"What kind of people live in Trinidad?" asked Nancy as the plane rose in the air.

"About a third of the people on the island are Hindus," replied Uncle Lee. "The upper classes of the remaining group are creoles of British, French, and Spanish blood. The lower classes are of Negro or mixed Negro origin, with a few Chinese."

A HINDU FAMILY IN TRINIDAD

The MacLarens looked down upon a gorgeous tropical island over which towered Mount Pelée. So this was Martinique!

Jimmy landed and escorted his friends through the French capital, Fort-de-France. It proved to be a quaint little town, almost like a country village, with its peaked roofs, its central square where the crowds gathered during leisure hours, and its barefooted women and children running after street venders. These good-natured fellows sold milk and confections. The happy citizens were, for the most part, black, and the women wore bright-colored fichus and skirts. Nowhere had Peter and Nancy seen a gayer, more care-free lot of people. As for the children, they danced happily about the visitors, curious but polite.

The two rivers between which the town had been built were named Monsieur and Madam. Very easy to remember! Easy to remember, too, was the marble statue of the Empress Josephine, first wife of Napoleon Bonaparte, in the middle of the public square. The people of Martinique were proud of the fact that the empress had been born on their little island.

Jimmy said that at the other end of the island could be seen the ruins of the city destroyed in 1902 by the eruption of Mount Pelée. Tourists were attracted by the volcanic specimens, but Jimmy said that the magenta bougainvillea that spread over the tumble-down houses was just as well worth seeing.

Jimmy brought his plane down at San Juan, the capital and largest city of the island of Puerto Rico. The second largest city, Ponce, he explained, was on the south.

Ewing Galloway

TOBACCO PLANTS UNDER NETTING

The MacLarens found the weather warm but not uncomfortable. They walked uptown, crowding along on the sidewalks. They saw many laden donkeys and burdened black men.

Outside the town were miles and miles of waving sugar cane. There were numerous tobacco farms. White netting protected the plants from the direct rays of the sun. Uncle Lee explained that the tobacco growers protected their plants in this way so that the tobacco would have a mild flavor. There was an air of lively prosperity that was surprising on a southern island.

"The United States has done a great deal to help Puerto Rico since it was ceded to us by Spain

in 1898," Uncle Lee remarked. "We've established
schools, built roads, and improved the railroads.
The farmers raise tobacco, coffee, cotton, and all
sorts of tropical fruits and vegetables in addition
to sugar. There's a ready market in the United
States for the winter-grown fruits and vegetables."

Jimmy persuaded the MacLarens to leave the
busy wharf where Puerto Rican products were
being loaded on ships for export, and again his
plane rose, this time its destination being Port-
au-Prince, the capital of Haiti.

"Port-au-Prince is a real city now," Jimmy
volunteered. "There are more than a hundred
thousand people here and it's one of the health-
iest spots in the West Indies."

Port-au-Prince, the capital of the Black Republic of Haiti, proved to be one of the strangest
cities the MacLarens had ever visited. For
one thing, the people were Negroes who spoke
French. There were, Uncle Lee said, 2,500,000
of them, and they occupied the western third
of the island of Hispaniola. They worshiped
black saints in a huge yellowish cathedral and
indulged in the sport of cock fighting, but on
the streets there were many beauty parlors and
cafes, while men marched along with golf clubs
and tennis rackets. There was also much talk
of horse racing. The Franco-Latin architecture
was appropriate and beautiful in this city of
sunshine and roses. The MacLarens strolled

James Sawders

A STREET IN PORT-AU-PRINCE

about the city, enjoying the busy crowds, and
later Uncle Lee hired a carriage to show Peter
and Nancy the stately homes of some of the black
aristocrats. Turrets and arbored patios gave
dignity to houses from whose gardens the odor
of jasmine often perfumed the air.

But a city was a city. The true life of the
people could best be studied in the country, Uncle
Lee maintained. On the road along which Uncle
Lee drove with Peter and Nancy walked many
straight, fine-looking black men and women. Don-

keys and mules were much more common than cars or carriages.

Nancy called out to Peter to watch a woman who was washing her clothes on the bank of a shallow stream. The MacLarens got out of the carriage and walked up one of the little lanes that opened off the main road. They came to a clay-thatched hut, set among fruit trees.

"This squatter's cabin," Uncle Lee observed, "is part of the real backbone of Haiti. While politicians scheme and make war, the native Haitian is self-sufficient. He has, you will notice, his flowering banana plant, his mango tree, his coffee shrub, and his garden plot where he grows his red beans. Over there you see his cow, munching coarse grass contentedly, and those pigs and chickens are his, too."

When Nancy saw the big family of black children, she wondered where the various members of the family slept at night. The hut, at best, could not have more than two small rooms. Uncle Lee explained that the turf outside made a good bed.

They got back into the carriage, and the two old horses presently brought the party to a market square.

"We'll find markets all over the island," Uncle Lee explained. "It is said that where there are a hundred people in Haiti there is a market. The native would rather bargain than eat. It is his most enjoyable pastime."

This particular market was a simple affair. There were no booths or tables. The sellers simply squatted on the ground and spread out their wares. Peter and Nancy walked between piles of oranges, breadfruit, dried nuts, and pawpaws. They examined crude pottery. They side-stepped live pigs and chickens and were offered fish and wilting vegetables. Some of the women were selling tallow, lard, and coconut oil. There were homemade cassava cookies and candies that Peter sampled, but Nancy contented herself with some lovely hibiscus flowers. Uncle Lee pointed out various herbs that were being sold as medicine.

Back in Port-au-Prince, the MacLarens joined Jimmy in a garden cafe where they enjoyed a French dinner that included ice cream.

After a restful night in a modern hotel, they decided to visit the Dominican Republic which occupied the eastern two-thirds of the island of Hispaniola.

"The peoples of the two countries are quite different," Uncle Lee announced at breakfast. "As you know, the people of Haiti are Negroes who speak French. Most of the people in the Dominican Republic are a mixed race, descendants of the natives, the early Spanish conquerors, and the Negroes. They speak Spanish!"

"The products are different as to quantity at least," Jimmy put in. "You'll see coffee trees all over Haiti, and it's well known that Haiti ships out over a million pounds of coffee a year. The

James Sawders

NANCY LIKED THE LOVELY HIBISCUS FLOWERS

Dominican Republic is most famous for its sugar. By the way, my plane won't be ready for some hours yet. I suggest that you make the trip to Santo Domingo by boat. There's a good little passenger steamer leaving very soon."

Within half an hour the MacLarens were

standing at the rail of the small steamer Jimmy had recommended, watching Port-au-Prince fade away. The sea was very blue, and the sun very bright.

Peter and Nancy strove to catch a glimpse of Santo Domingo City, now called Ciudad Trujillo. But it was not until the boat had made its way around a high cliff that jutted out into the Caribbean that they suddenly saw the whole city rising from the coral cliffs and spreading out over the low hills. Uncle Lee said that farther inland were high mountains. But the city held the children's interest, the oldest city in the Western Hemisphere founded by Europeans. It was in 1496, just four years after America was discovered, Uncle Lee told them, that a band of Spanish colonists had settled there.

The MacLarens followed the passengers down the gangplank and walked ashore at a spot not far from where Columbus had landed. The ancient main gate of the city lay ahead, and through it pressed the motley traffic. There were cars, ponies, donkeys, wagons, and pedestrians black and white, invariably laden with bundles. On the wagons red peppers glowed, jute sacks rose in piles, and pineapples and melons were seen in containers.

The new buildings of Spanish architecture, as well as the old, seemed a part of the past, for they fitted into their surroundings as though they had always been there. Turning a corner, the MacLarens came, quite unexpectedly, upon a central plaza. Its paths were fragrant with tropical bloom and alive with color. Comfortable marble benches invited the newcomers, but Peter and Nancy broke away from Uncle Lee to run toward the statue of Columbus in the center of the plaza. The gesture of the great conqueror bespoke pride in Ciudad Trujillo, and the lifelike figures of the Indians at the base added to the dignity and beauty of the monument.

Behind the memorial stood the Cathedral of Santo Domingo. Uncle Lee said that the architecture was Spanish Renaissance, and its lovely design placed it among the best of the early churches.

Passing through the shadowy entrance, the MacLarens gazed long upon the white marble tomb where the remains of Columbus had lain.

"Columbus could have been enshrined in no lovelier place," Nancy decided, and Peter and Uncle Lee agreed.

"But Spain claimed her famous explorer," Uncle Lee added. "After the Spanish-American War, the remains of Columbus were transferred to Seville where they have been enshrined permanently."

ISLES OF ENCHANTMENT

" JAMAICA," Uncle Lee observed, as Peter and Nancy sat on the white sand at Trujillo and watched the green water curl into white foam on the beach, "has fine harbors, sixteen in all. Its climate is almost perfect, and its plains are exceptionally fertile."

He scanned the horizon for sight of Jimmy Dustin's plane which he expected any minute.

"Plains!" Peter scoffed. "I thought there were green mountains in Jamaica—and jungles."

"There are," Uncle Lee agreed affably. "But mountains do not preclude plains, do they?"

"Here comes Jimmy!" Nancy shouted. "You two may as well stop arguing. We'll see what Jamaica is like in a few hours."

The MacLaren party made a glorious trip over blue-green water with Jimmy Dustin and landed on a white sand beach not far from Kingston. Kingston lay on the south coast in the eastern part of the island, a fine and beautiful city.

The one fact that impressed Peter and Nancy more than anything else, as they strolled about the streets of the capital of Jamaica, was that it was definitely English; English in architecture, in landscape gardening, and in law-abiding order. In sharp contrast to the colored people who ambled along on their way to the market or to plantations

were the English bobbies in their immaculate
white uniforms.

Uncle Lee told the children that an earthquake
in 1907 had almost destroyed Kingston. They
could hardly believe it, although the buildings
did look very new in contrast to the other places
the MacLarens had visited. Uncle Lee added
that, in rebuilding the city, special plans were
used to make the buildings earthquake proof.

The business places were smart, the white
population much like that seen on any metro-
politan street, and the homes of the wealthy
most attractive. There were many picturesque
Tudor homes, but the children were more interested in the tumble-down huts on the outskirts
of the city.

Over a fine road the MacLarens drove out to
view Spanish Town, once the capital of Jamaica.
They walked in the stately ruins of King's House.
They sat for a while in the cool quiet of the
cathedral, and then strolled through the plaza.
Peter contemplated the Hanging Tree where
many a pirate had swung in the early days.

"Uncle Lee, you were right," Peter admitted
as the car turned off on a country road. "There
are plains back from the town, plains that run
into the hill country. What wonderful farms!"

The farms offered a wide variety of produce:
bananas and coconuts on vast plantations, and
pineapples, oranges, and limes on less extensive
estates. Uncle Lee said that in the interior the

Ewing Galloway

CARRYING BANANAS TO MARKET

logwood tree grew luxuriantly, and while the
wood is exported, the making of logwood extract
for dye is a valuable industry. There were great
fields of sugar cane, uplands where coffee trees
grew, and a number of cacao bushes, as well as
cinnamon, nutmeg, and allspice trees.

"Allspice trees?" asked Peter. "I thought allspice was cinnamon, cloves, and nutmeg ground
together."

"Tastes like it," answered Uncle Lee, "but allspice comes from a little berry that grows on an
evergreen tree called pimento or allspice. The

berries are picked green, dried, and their two little brown seeds, when ground, make the allspice that is used for seasoning. Lots of ginger is exported, too."

The entire country was a sea of brilliant green color. Everywhere Negroes carried produce on their heads, walking erect.

"Everything under the sun is here!" Peter exulted. "Jimmy says you can even get salt along the coast."

"Any ocean coast has salt," Nancy affirmed. "That doesn't make salt a commercial product."

"It does here," Peter maintained. "Jamaica exports at least a million bushels a year. Jimmy says so."

Before leaving Jamaica, the MacLarens and Jimmy made a back-country trip. That trip was full of delightful surprises. They visited cold and hot springs, viewed fairylike waterfalls, and walked along the cliffs of steep gorges. They made a trek into the jungle where they stared up at the jungle growth and exclaimed at the exquisite orchids hanging in the trees. Returning to Kingston, they visited the Hope Gardens and saw in the conservatories and outdoor gardens the very plants and trees they had seen growing wild.

"Havana, Cuba!" Jimmy was preparing to take off with the MacLarens from Kingston. "It is one of the gay cities of the Western Hemisphere!"

"Cuba is our sugar bowl!" Peter added dryly. "That's the first thing I ever learned in school about it. We could depend on Cuba for sugar and tobacco. Many of our manufacturers use tobacco grown in Cuba in making their good cigars, the kind you could give away at Christmas. I read that the finest tobacco in the world is grown in Cuba."

"Anyway, Cuba is the biggest and most important island of the West Indies," Jimmy concluded. "In its landlocked bays are very fine harbors. Its mountain streams, tumbling down through rich valleys, are delightful to see. And when you come to Havana, you'll see a city that will stand comparison with any city on earth."

"You ought to write travel folders, Jimmy," Nancy teased. "Why didn't we keep such a remarkable possession as Jimmy describes, Uncle Lee?"

Uncle Lee hesitated.

"Spain surrendered Cuba to the United States in 1898," he began. "We improved her schools, built roads, and developed her industries. We made her see what she had: sugar, tobacco, tropical fruits, and vegetables. Then there were hardwoods and metals such as copper, manganese, and iron. We taught her to use asphalt for her roads. Like a good neighbor and friend, we helped her get on her feet. Then we withdrew our soldiers from her soil when she chose to become an independent republic."

THE CAPITOL BUILDING IN HAVANA

"At school last year we had a moving picture about Cuba," Peter said. "It showed some of the improvements that were made in Cuba while the island was held 'in trust' by the United States."

Jimmy brought his plane down at Havana, after circling over the city. Peter and Nancy were amazed at its size, and at the handsome, modern buildings.

"A seventh of all the people of Cuba live in Havana," explained Uncle Lee. "Rich planters who own these great country places often have a town residence, too, and nearly everybody at some time or other has business in Havana, the capital."

The *Prado*, a boulevard park in the shopping district, became the scene of a daily walk during the week the MacLaren party remained in Havana. Peter spent much time with Jimmy down on the wharves watching the stevedores load sugar, tobacco, and cigars. The entire party spent half a day in a great cigar factory where hundreds of workmen rolled cigars in a large room. In the center was a platform on which a man sat reading in Spanish. The MacLarens were told that the laborers contributed a few cents a week to hire this man to read to them while they worked. He usually began with the morning paper and then read magazines or books all day. Peter and Nancy could not understand a word but they thought it was a good idea. It kept the work from being monotonous.

"Sugar and tobacco!" Peter decided. "And tobacco and sugar! That's Cuba! It's the world's sugar bowl, all right!"

"Cuba, and India, too," Uncle Lee amended. "India has helped to fill the world's sugar bowl, too. The two countries have been rivals for years, often with Cuba leading. By the way, remember that the sugar comes from the eastern half of the island, and tobacco comes from the western part. The Cubans say that tobacco is king and sugar is queen."

The wealth of the city of Havana was ap-

James Sawders

HAULING SUGAR CANE TO THE MILL

parent, not only in the thriving shopping districts but in the residential districts as well.
There were palatial homes with their patios and
gardens hidden behind stucco walls. In the older
part of the city the streets were crooked and so
very narrow that a person on one of the over-
hanging balconies could easily shake hands with
someone on the balcony opposite. Everywhere
Spanish architecture was evident in latticed windows, wrought-iron balconies, and heavy, carved
doors. Rose and jasmine perfume filled the air.
When the afternoon siesta was over, the city

James Sawders

MORRO CASTLE AT HAVANA

would come to life. The sidewalk cafes would begin to fill, and the shops would begin to sell French perfumes, laces, and jewels across their counters, along with more utilitarian merchandise.

Each evening the MacLarens drove along the Prado or out upon the beautiful *Malecon* drive. One morning they visited Morro Castle, which looked as though it were still grimly defending the town, and afterward they swam out from the beach with hundreds of vacationists who were enjoying life as never before.

But Jimmy Dustin kept saying that the plane

was ready to go, and Uncle Lee reluctantly
admitted that he had business to look after in
Florida.

Nassau in the Bahamas was to be the last
stop before the homeward flight.

"The fashionable Bahamas," Jimmy called the
islands, and added, "Nassau is an all-year pleasure resort. This trip seems to be ending in play
rather than study."

Peter and Nancy laughed, for they knew that
the Isles of Enchantment in the Caribbean had
given them much food for thought as well as
enjoyment.

As the plane soared above the Bahamas, Peter
and Nancy expressed amazement at the number
of little islands that comprised the group. Uncle
Lee told them that there were about twenty-nine
islands, and three thousand bays and islets. Some
of the islands were too small to live on, and many
were just large enough for a plantation or two.
There were villages on some of the islands.
Usually these little villages were near orange or
pineapple plantations.

"A great deal of sisal fiber is produced in the
islands," Uncle Lee remarked. "And remember
that the Bahamas are coral islands. Millions of
little coral animals produced these reefs over a
period of many years."

Jimmy brought his plane down near the
wharves of Nassau, the chief city of the Bahamas. The wharves were piled high with sisal

Ewing Galloway

WEAVING SISAL FIBERS INTO HATS AND BAGS

fiber in dark brown bundles, green oranges, large pineapples, crates of tomatoes, and sponges. Nancy stepped away from some large turtles that had been turned over on their backs to prevent their getting away.

Peter said, "Turtle soup!" and he, too, backed away.

The beaches were of white sand and pink-tinged coral, and the clear green water broke into white foam at the children's feet. Farther out the water appeared rose and orange and lavender.

Nassau, the MacLarens were to learn, is noted for its gorgeous colors and for its sunsets.

In contrast to the busy wharves the city seemed singularly quiet, especially as evening drew near. The sound of the surf could still be heard, and there was a whispering in the swaying palms. An atmosphere of peace enveloped the island. Even the ruins of the fortresses spoke of a forgotten past when pirates swarmed the seas and overran the island. But the memories were dim. The crystal caves and the sea gardens that could be viewed in glass-bottomed boats belonged to the morrow for the MacLarens.

Two days later, refreshed, stimulated, and happy, the MacLaren party in Jimmy Dustin's little plane rose over the fragrant, lovely island to sail above sparkling waters toward home.

FISHES, APPLES, AND FOXES

THE world was a sea of white fog as Jimmy Dustin flew steadily northward. The three MacLarens, Peter, Nancy, and Uncle Lee, seated in the tiny cabin behind Jimmy Dustin, huddled together in the cold.

"It's a good thing I had these new instruments installed before we left Miami," Jimmy remarked. "When we stopped to refuel at Newark, the mechanic said they were in perfect working order. I hope he was right because I'm flying by them. We're near Halifax, I'm sure."

Soon the fog broke, and from the low-flying plane Peter and Nancy saw a land of small, rounded hills and broad valleys such as they had seen in New England. Uncle Lee explained that in this oldest part of the continent weather had worn down what were once mountain peaks, filled up valleys, and carried much silt to the sea to make more land.

"Timber is plentiful here and lumbering is an important industry," Jimmy explained, "yet most of the inhabitants are not lumbermen but fishermen. There must be fifty thousand of them. When you eat creamed codfish on your baked potatoes next winter, remember Nova Scotia!"

The plane droned on and Jimmy announced, "We're flying along the southeastern coast."

Ewing Galloway

PREPARING CODFISH FOR DRYING

"Look below!" Peter exclaimed suddenly. "A big city with dozens of ships in the harbor!"

"Halifax!" Jimmy shouted. "It is the largest city of the Maritime Provinces and lies closer to England than any port on the Canadian mainland."

"Maritime?" Nancy wrinkled her brow.

"Maritime, of course," Peter spoke up. "That means 'bordering on the sea.' There's Nova Scotia with Cape Breton Island, New Brunswick, and Prince Edward Island."

"Brilliant geographer!" Uncle Lee pronounced.

Ewing Galloway

THE WATERFRONT IN HALIFAX

The plane descended into a splendid harbor on whose placid waters great ocean-going liners nosed up against big freighters and fishing schooners. There were many sailors on the docks, but few soldiers. Uncle Lee said that Halifax had once been an important military city, but that it was no longer garrisoned as it used to be.

"The chief British military and naval station in Canada is here in Halifax," Uncle Lee continued. "Now, however, the principal interests are commerce and shipping.

"In the early days Nova Scotia's shipbuilding yards were crowded with wooden ships; her skippers in their sailing vessels sailed all over the seven seas, and Canada became for a time the fourth maritime nation in the world. Among the city's greatest sons was Samuel Cunard who founded the first regular steamship service across the Atlantic."

Ashore Peter and Nancy looked about in amazement at the great quantities of freight piled up on the wharves. A small boy who had seen the MacLaren party land said, "Hello, birdlings!" and the MacLarens, without more ado, began asking questions.

"What is shipped from this port?" inquired Peter.

"Fish oil, along with dried fish, hides, skins, wool, lumber, grain, and in the fall, apples," answered the boy.

"Apples!" Nancy exclaimed. "Where do they come from?"

"Have you ever heard of Evangeline?" The boy looked eager.

Peter and Nancy nodded.

"Apples come from the part of Nova Scotia that's known as the home of the Acadians," the boy explained. "Evangeline was an Acadian, as you know. We're French, and my ancestors were here long before the land fell into English hands. You haven't seen the Annapolis Valley?"

"If we haven't seen the Annapolis Valley, we

Ewing Galloway
SPRINGTIME IN THE LAND OF EVANGELINE

haven't seen anything, I suppose," Peter teased.

"No, sir, you haven't!" the boy said, seriously. "If you think Halifax a great city, you should see our city in the Annapolis Valley."

As he walked about the wharves with Peter and Nancy, the boy went on, "The French called our city Port Royal, but we call it Annapolis Royal. You must see it. It's one of the oldest towns on this continent north of Florida. There are stone ramparts still standing, and I can show you the lilies of France stamped on the hinges of historic doors."

By the time Uncle Lee and Jimmy had attended to having the plane refueled, Peter and Nancy were bubbling over with enthusiasm.

They knew they would not be disappointed when they should fly over the country of the Acadians and look down on small, well-kept farms with their beautiful orchards. In May and June, Jimmy declared, they would be all pink and white and fragrant.

Warmed and fed at Halifax, the little party was soon ready to leave. Jimmy turned the plane northeast, flying as low as he dared to show Peter and Nancy the beautiful Bras d'Or lakes. The blue, heavily-wooded lakes looked remote and yet so inviting that Nancy declared she wished they might spend a summer there.

"Evidently you're not the first person to have that idea," Uncle Lee mused. "Dr. Alexander Graham Bell, who invented the telephone, chose this spot for his summer residence. He and Mrs. Bell are both buried on the mountainside overlooking the lake."

Soon Uncle Lee was pointing out Louisburg, the town with the strong fortress that had held out against the English for two months in 1758.

Flying away from this little town which had once been so valiant, Jimmy indicated the positions of great coal mines near Sydney, the largest city in Cape Breton.

"These are the only coal deposits in North America which lie conveniently near the sea,"

Uncle Lee explained. "They make Sydney a great industrial center. As you see, it's at the entrance to the Gulf of St. Lawrence."

"We'll refuel here and then fly farther northeastward to sight Newfoundland," said Jimmy.

"Wonderful!" Peter shouted.

"Provided the weather's good," Uncle Lee added, as they descended.

It was foggy and very cold as the plane flew across Cabot Strait toward Newfoundland.

Jimmy called out, "I think you'll see the peak of an iceberg soon."

"Guessing?" Peter sat forward eagerly. "Or are you sure, Jimmy?"

"Fairly sure," Jimmy replied. "The fog is opening up."

Within a few minutes the sun broke through the heavy mist, and below the plane the sharp, pointed top of an iceberg appeared, the great bulk of it beneath a sea on which wide swells ran in rhythmic beauty.

Jimmy turned the plane landward and presently announced, "We're over the Grand Banks."

"I don't see any land." Nancy strained for a view of shorelines.

"Land!" Jimmy chuckled like an old sea captain in a storybook. "Your geography, my lass, is very meager in its scope. The Grand Banks are land, I might concede, but they're under water."

"The sea is very shallow here," Uncle Lee explained. "Underneath is a plain about two hundred miles long and seventy miles wide. The Arctic current flows down over the Banks, bringing with it what may look like slime to you; but to the codfish, the herring, and the lobsters, it looks like a banquet. That slime contains much sea life, all of which is good fish food. By the way, Newfoundland is not a part of Canada but a separate colony; the oldest, in fact, in the British Empire. However, Great Britain very generously allows us to fish in her waters."

Nancy interrupted Uncle Lee with a shout of delight.

"Uncle Lee!" she cried. "Look out there! A whole fleet of fishing schooners!"

Peter and Nancy stared, a widening grin on Peter's face as the fleet came into view: small, sturdy boats with sea-washed decks where hearty men in oilskins were handling nets. Several looked up and saluted the airplane. The MacLarens saluted in return.

"I'd guess that fishing is an important industry in Newfoundland," remarked Peter.

"Right," was Uncle Lee's reply. "And the fishing is not limited to cod as most people imagine. The salmon industry is gaining constantly in importance, and I can see a splendid future for it in Newfoundland."

"Salmon are interesting fish," continued Uncle Lee. "The young fish live in fresh water. Then about May they usually migrate to the sea. But

Ewing Galloway

SALMON JUMPING THE FALLS OF A RIVER
IN NEWFOUNDLAND

at spawning time they always return to the
waters from which they came, to lay their eggs."

Jimmy swung back again westward and southward toward Prince Edward Island. Nancy
settled comfortably beside Peter.

"Those islands on the right," called out Jimmy,
"are the Magdalens, a part of Quebec Province.
They are inhabited by descendants of the Acadians and are all that's left now of the romantic
spirit of Acadia."

"The island's only a little bigger than Delaware," Uncle Lee informed Peter and Nancy, "but we don't want to miss the Garden Province."

"Does it deserve the name?" Nancy inquired.

"We'll let you judge for yourself," Uncle Lee decided.

Separated from the mainland by Northumberland Strait lay the green island, so long and narrow that the water could be reached in a very short time from any part. The scenery was much like that of New England.

Jimmy brought his plane down in the harbor of Charlottetown and Uncle Lee hired a car to show Peter and Nancy some of the fine farms with their vegetable gardens, their apple, plum, and pear orchards, and their acres of berry bushes. The cattle and sheep looked fat and contented, and Jimmy said that Prince Edward Island was one of the best dairy lands on earth.

Stopping at a farm, the party was shown the utmost hospitality. They learned that in the town close by there was a co-operative dairy that handled the milk, making it into butter and cheese.

The small son of the house begged Peter and Nancy to go out into the barnyard to see his pets. The pets proved to be two silver foxes which the boy's father said were very valuable.

"You'll find many fur farms in Canada," he told them. "This is just a start for us. My brother over at the other end of the island raises otter. And I know a fellow who raises beaver

Ewing Galloway

SILVER FOXES

and mink. Some fur farms have success with muskrat and skunk, but most of the big fur farms on Prince Edward Island are fox farms."

"Raising fur-bearing animals is a paying venture," Jimmy decided. "And it will continue to be, especially when the wild ones grow scarcer."

They drove into the capital, Charlottetown, with its wide streets, great trees, and lovely homes. In the heart of the city stood the fine old Parliament Building.

"You know, children," Uncle Lee told them, "Prince Edward Island is known in Canada as

'the Cradle of Confederation' because it was right
here in this old stone Parliament Building that
the plan of uniting all of the provinces into the
Dominion of Canada came into being."

Peter and Nancy were so enthusiastic about
Charlottetown that Jimmy said, "You remind
me of the French sailors who first entered the
harbor."

"In what way?" Nancy asked.

"They liked the place so well, even before it
was a town," Jimmy explained, "that they called
it *Port la Joie*, the 'Port of Joy.'"

"It's a perfect name for it," Peter decided.

Rising from Prince Edward Island like a soaring gull, the seaplane crossed Northumberland
Strait, a corner of Nova Scotia, Minas Basin,
and the Annapolis Valley, sweet with orchard
bloom, just as Peter and Nancy had known it
would be. It sped across the Bay of Fundy from
Nova Scotia to New Brunswick whose forests,
Uncle Lee said, joined those of Maine. Peter
and Nancy looked down first on fishing boats,
and later on beautiful forests where men would
be cutting trees in the fall.

"Lumbering such as we used to see in Minnesota and Wisconsin," Uncle Lee observed. "The
trees are mostly spruce, but there are a number
of fir, hemlock, and cedar trees as well as harder
woods like oak and birch."

"It's a pity we can't visit New Brunswick's
capital, Fredericton, and the lovely Matapedia

Ewing Galloway

A PULP AND PAPER PLANT

Valley, or busy Moncton," cried Jimmy. "But I am going to circle over the harbor of St. John."

Peter and Nancy could see that Saint John, another old city, was located at the mouth of the St. John River on the Bay of Fundy.

"At high tide," Jimmy explained to the excited children, "the bay is actually higher than the river. This means that the tide pours up the river and turns the cascades above Saint John into what are called the Reversing Falls. It is one of the strange sights of the world to watch those falls going backward at high tide."

"It's because the Bay of Fundy tides are the highest in the world," added Uncle Lee.

Peter and Nancy had a swift vision of logs in the river, a busy sawmill, and ships waiting at the wharves for their cargoes of lumber, wood-pulp, and wood products such as boards, sashes, boxes, and shingles. But soon their thoughts were turned toward that greatest of all Canadian rivers, the St. Lawrence.

TODAY'S QUEBEC
WITH YESTERDAY'S CHARM

THEY sighted the river after flying for hours over the dense forests of New Brunswick. Cruising southwest along the Gaspé Coast, Peter and Nancy peered eagerly at the broad river below.

"We can't see everything," Uncle Lee told them regretfully. "But some day we'll visit Gaspè itself, so lovely a village that its fame has spread all over America. The people have not adopted many modern conveniences. Outdoor ovens are still used for baking bread. Gaspé has a wonderful salmon hatchery that I'd like to show you, too. And away out in the gulf is the big island of Anticosti, once owned entirely by a famous French chocolate king and now being developed for pulp and paper. Beyond that is the Strait of Belle Isle which divides Newfoundland from Labrador. Some day we'll take a cruise to Labrador from Montreal to see how the Indian and Eskimo children live. And we'll visit the world-famous Grenfell missions along the rocky coast. It will be great fun sailing on the very fringe of the Arctic, seeing the northern lights, the short twilight nights, perhaps an iceberg or two, and seals and polar bears. But we can't make it on this trip."

Ewing Galloway

OUTDOOR OVENS ARE STILL USED

The plane descended near the shore off Father Point, where incoming ocean liners pick up their river pilots. It came to a stop at Rimouski wharf for refueling.

A brief glimpse of this typical French-Canadian town and they were off again, heading across the St. Lawrence, many miles broad at this point.

Soon they saw the great Laurentian Mountains, and at the mouth of an immense canyon a tiny village shining in the summer sun.

"That's Tadoussac," exclaimed Jimmy as he circled over the prettiest summer resort they had ever seen. "Tadoussac is very old. When Car-

tier first saw it in 1535, it was a big Indian camp
of over a thousand people. And that great canyon between the mountains is the mighty Saguenay River, said to be a mile deep. Cruise ships
from Montreal sail up as far as Capes Trinity
and Eternity. The scenery is grander than that
of the famous fiords of Norway. The Saguenay
flows down from Lake St. John; the upper falls
are used for power plants to run big aluminum
works and paper mills."

Away they flew westward, over fashionable
Murray Bay with its luxurious hotel, the Manoir
Richelieu, past many historic French-Canadian
towns nestling under steep, forested cliffs.

"This is the way Jacques Cartier, the dis-
coverer of the St. Lawrence, approached Quebec,"
announced Jimmy as he roared his plane over
the green Isle of Orleans.

As they neared the western end of the isle,
they caught sight of a tumultuous waterfall on
their right, where the Montmorency tumbles over
the cliff into the St. Lawrence.

"I know!" cried Peter excitedly, "Montmorency
Falls, over a hundred feet higher than Niagara!"

As they approached, Quebec seemed like a city
of the Middle Ages, perched on the great rock
rising almost sheer from the river.

The children cried out in ecstasy. Uncle Lee
roused himself, pleased at their excitement.

"So this is Quebec! Neighbor, I salute you!"
exclaimed Uncle Lee.

Ewing Galloway

MONTMORENCY FALLS

"Quebec would feel quite elated if she were a queen and could see your expression of admiration," Nancy decided.

"She is a queen," Uncle Lee maintained. "Within just the last few years Quebec Province

Canadian Travel Bureau

QUEBEC FROM THE ST. LAWRENCE RIVER

has started an industrial expansion to be proud of. In fact, all of Canada is advancing steadily in manufacturing and farming. Montreal is the leading wheat port of the world, and the inland provinces are supplying paper for all of us. You'll see many mills producing sulphite wood-pulp to be made into rayon. These mills are run by water power."

"White coal!" Peter interrupted. "That's what they call the water power. Once Jimmy told me that the tumbling rivers from the Laurentian Mountains supply the power for the mills and for the shoe factories which are becoming more and more numerous in Quebec."

Ewing Galloway

THE HARBOR OF QUEBEC

Jimmy brought the plane down in the harbor, sending up sprays of clear, sparkling diamonds over the wings. A little boat chugged out to tow the plane up to the *Quai du Roi.*

In a few minutes the MacLaren party was visiting an old market place where the country people sold their produce. Many of the fruits and vegetables arranged on tables were protected from the sun by large umbrellas.

The MacLarens walked gaily along *Rue de Notre Dame,* Quebec's oldest street. It was a mysterious street, shadowed by a rocky cliff on one side and old stone buildings on the other. One short block, and then the sunlight fell on a fine, open square named after Champlain.

Ewing Galloway

AN OLD MARKET PLACE IN QUEBEC

It was high noon and the Angelus rang out from an ancient church near by. It made them think somehow of Champlain and his struggles with the hostile Indians in the early days.

"A walled city!" Nancy squinted up at the fortress walls as she climbed up Mountain Hill or *Cote de la Montagne.* "I feel as though it were 1608 instead of 1938 when I tread these cobblestones."

Passing the magnificent Basilica and the Cardinal's Palace, they finally reached the beautiful Dufferin Terrace promenade. It was built along

the top of the rock from the great hotel, Château
Frontenac, to the foot of the even greater heights
of the fortified citadel. From this vantage point
they looked down hundreds of feet over Lower
Town, across the river and at Lévis opposite.

Uncle Lee chuckled. "You should see this terrace in winter! It's turned into a wonderful
swift toboggan slide. In fact, Quebec's a great
spot for winter holidays, with its dog-sled derbies,
snowshoeing, and skiing.

"Lévis, on the opposite shore there, has ship-
yards; you can see them. When Wolfe attacked
Quebec, he shelled the city with artillery from
those heights above the town there."

Uncle Lee then hired a two-wheeled carriage
called a *calèche*. Perched high on its quaint
seats, the party made a sight-seeing tour of the
city. Their French-Canadian cabby proved most
courteous and full of information, talking in
broken English.

They visited the old citadel, walked along its
fortified road built between two rocky walls, and
watched a battalion of French-Canadians drilling.
They drove slowly and reverently down the
Avenue des Braves whose flowering rose trees
on either side had been planted in memory of
Quebec's soldiers who were killed during the
Great War. They stood on the Plains of Abraham by the monuments to the great generals
Wolfe and Montcalm whom Quebec honors with
equal affection. They stood on the campus and

Ewing Galloway

SOUS LE FORT STREET IN QUEBEC

viewed the buildings of Laval University as Uncle
Lee explained that it was organized by royal
charter from Queen Victoria of England in 1852.
They visited the well-known Church of the

Ewing Galloway

WOLFE MONUMENT ON THE PLAINS OF ABRAHAM

Perpetual Adoration where devout nuns, in half-hour relays, keep a never-ending prayer alive. They saw a genuine Rubens painting inside a church that was old even when the British took Quebec. They drove through the quaint country-side to the famous shrine of Ste. Anne de Beaupré exclaiming with delight when they saw boys driving dogcarts. Old women at spinning wheels were seen on verandas, and once they caught sight of a plow drawn by two sleepy oxen!

"What a dear, quaint country!" cried Nancy.

"It's really old France in the New World," Uncle Lee remarked.

Against the granite entrance of the Hôtel de Ville stood a statue of Louis Hébert.

"The first farmer citizen of Quebec!" Uncle Lee announced. "Once he was a pharmacist in Paris, but he left his mortar and pestle for a spade and plow."

"What names are these?" Nancy asked as she examined a bronze plate on the base of the statue.

"French Canada's 'Mayflower' list," Uncle Lee explained. "Those are the names of pioneers who came over between 1615 and 1641. Eleven of them! The sixty names below are those of pioneers who arrived after 1641—within the following twenty-five years."

"Most of those names," Jimmy declared, "may be found today on the stores and offices of the city of Quebec. Names like Cote, Belanger, Langlois, Boucher, and Hébert are well known. The French Canadians love their vigorous climate, and big families are common."

Then, to the delight of Peter and Nancy, he recited a Kipling limerick:

> There was a young boy of Quebec,
> Who fell through some ice to his neck.
>   When asked, "Are you friz?"
>   He replied, "Yes, I is,
> But we don't call this cold in Quebec."

Peter and Nancy looked down on the old city before descending to the St. Lawrence. They watched it in the afternoon sunshine stretching up toward Montreal, and they were told that along its banks were hundreds of fertile farms and pretty villages.

"Just how large is Quebec Province, Uncle Lee?" Peter inquired. "It looks pretty big on Jimmy's map."

"The whole province is nearly one fourth as large as the United States," Uncle Lee said. "But it's just the narrow strip of land along the St. Lawrence that is well populated. The rest is largely 'bush.'"

On the banks of the St. Lawrence there was a great deal of life and activity. Ships and ferries came and went along the river.

Uncle Lee pointed northward with a wide gesture.

"Out there," he declared, "are deep forests, steep hills, mountains, and swift streams. You'll find lumber, fur-bearing animals, and valuable minerals in that so-called bush."

Uncle Lee went on to explain that this region beyond the river was called the Laurentian Mountains and was one of the oldest rock formations of the American continent.

"But the old Laurentian Highland is pretty much worn down," Jimmy added. "I've flown over the region and seen its rolling hills, broad, open valleys, and hundreds of lakes."

The four members of the party stood quietly on the quay watching the boats being loaded.

"Those boats are going out with supplies for winter camps," Jimmy explained. "Much logging is done in Quebec."

"That boat," Peter declared, "isn't handling supplies for a lumber camp."

"You're right, Peter," Jimmy acknowledged as a heavily laden barge nosed in. "It isn't. It's bringing in asbestos. Asbestos is mined in very few places on this earth. It may surprise you to learn that nearly all the asbestos in the world comes from the Thetford Mines, south of the St. Lawrence River. The province of Quebec may just naturally give you gold, silver, copper, nickel, and iron, but that's not surprising. Many metals are often found in mountainous country. But Quebec is unique in having asbestos mines."

"Our new furnace pipes at home are wrapped in asbestos," Peter remarked.

"Never has a better means of insulation been found. Asbestos keeps heat from escaping," Uncle Lee put in. "Asbestos in its raw state is found in rock. This rock is crushed and screened. Then, by means of vacuum fans, the asbestos fiber is separated from the rock itself. Finally it is graded, bagged, and sent to factories to be woven into cloth."

As they talked, they watched two saucy tugs work a steamer from Europe alongside the harbor breakwater.

"That's your boat," Jimmy declared.

"Our boat?" Peter and Nancy were incredulous.

"Your boat," Jimmy insisted. "Uncle Lee is going to take you to Montreal by steamer while I remain behind to recondition my plane."

THREE CANADIAN CITIES

THE great liner glided out of the harbor past the towering Citadel Rock. The MacLarens waved farewell to Dufferin Terrace far above them. Soon they were passing Wolfe's Cove, and the sight brought to mind the statues of Wolfe and Montcalm they had seen on the Plains of Abraham. What a night that must have been in 1769, when Wolfe and his men climbed silently up that slope to surprise the besieged Frenchmen next morning! How amazed Wolfe would be today to see here, on that very spot, this immense dock and shed and the great steamships moored alongside them!

"Where are all those boats going, Uncle Lee?" asked Peter.

"Probably they are going down the river to Baie Comeau to pick up cargoes of pulpwood which will be made into newsprint, the paper used in the printing of newspapers," said Uncle Lee.

"Much of the wood used in the manufacture of newsprint is spruce and balsam. Wood from many acres of forest is required to make enough paper for one Sunday edition."

"I'd like to live in a lumber camp," Peter declared. "Even forty below wouldn't scare me. Are the paper mills near the lumber camps?"

"Some of them are," Uncle Lee answered. Perhaps these ships will take their loads of pulp-wood to great paper mills like the one located at Thorold on the Welland Canal. Niagara Falls furnishes cheap power for use in this mill. Cheap power means cheap paper, and this is important to the people of the United States since we use about half the world's output of paper."

"Do we use most of the world's aluminum ware, too?" Peter inquired. "Jimmy says that Arvida in the Lake St. John region is famous for aluminum."

"That's right," Uncle Lee agreed. "Arvida, on the upper reaches of the Saguenay River, is a new city built for making aluminum. We got a glimpse of it at Tadoussac, you remember."

Suddenly Peter shouted, "Look! we're going to pass under the Quebec Bridge!"

They all gasped, like most of the other passengers on deck, as the ship approached the bridge. Surely the tall masts could never pass under it! Yet, as they held their breath and waited for the expected crash, the great ship passed silently and easily beneath those huge girders that spanned the river.

"That's a famous optical illusion that never fails to scare passengers," chuckled Uncle Lee. "That bridge, by the way, is a real triumph of engineering, although it collapsed twice while under construction. It has one of the longest cantilever spans in the world."

Ewing Galloway

THE QUEBEC BRIDGE

The trip to Montreal was most interesting. The travelers passed Three Rivers, a great pulp and paper city, so large that they imagined they were already arriving at Montreal. They could easily see the three rivers which joined the St. Lawrence at this point.

They passed through Lake St. Peter—a widening of the river—saw busy Sorel at the mouth of the historic Richelieu River, and came so close to the south shore in places that they could almost shout to people ashore. At last the pleasant cruise ended as they sailed into the busy harbor of

Montreal—the largest inland port in the world and the second largest French-speaking city.

The great city, with its skyscrapers, churches, universities, and immense factories, climbed up from the water front around the slopes of Mount Royal. On the top of the forested mountain they saw a great cross which was lighted at night.

Uncle Lee took the children for a carriage drive up through Mount Royal Park to the Lookout on the summit. From this great height they looked down on the vast city, the great St. Lawrence River like a white ribbon in the distance still stretching westward toward Ontario and the Great Lakes. Beyond lay rich farm lands of the eastern townships, and farther still in the blue haze rose the Adirondack Mountains in their own United States.

Across the river were two great bridges, with wedge-shaped piers.

"They are the queerest-shaped piers I ever saw!" Peter was puzzled.

"They're in the shape of big plowshares," Uncle Lee explained. "When the ice rushes against them in the spring they have to be able to meet the impact."

The MacLarens' driver, another cheery French-Canadian, pointed out some of the high spots in the city below. He told them of the Château de Ramezay where Benjamin Franklin had once set up a printing press, of the celebrated Lachine Rapids on the river above the city, of St. James'

Ewing Galloway

THE CATHEDRAL OF ST. JAMES

Cathedral, built in the style of St. Peter's in Rome and a third its size, and of many historic relics of old Montreal.

"I'd like to visit Montreal in winter," Peter

Canadian Travel Bureau

OTTAWA FROM THE AIR

decided. "Then we could ski, skate, snowshoe, and toboggan. It's a great place for sports. Well, Uncle Lee, where do we go from here? Up the St. Lawrence?"

"We'll go to Ottawa!" Uncle Lee answered. "The capital of Canada! We'll go by bus, for a change, up the lovely Ottawa Valley."

Ontario, Uncle Lee informed the children, was the province in which Ottawa was situated. He called Ontario the heart of Canada, where lived a third of the Dominion's people and where much of her wealth was found.

Ewing Galloway

THE FEDERAL HOUSES OF PARLIAMENT IN OTTAWA

Peter and Nancy liked Ottawa, a regal city built on the high west bank of the broad Ottawa River which raced at its feet. They admired the Chaudière Falls, the wooded parks near the city, and the magnificent government buildings.

Peter wanted to spend most of his time among the lumber piles near the river. He enjoyed the smell of freshly-cut wood, which made him a little homesick for the farm; he liked to walk between the long, high piles of lumber. It was like walking through narrow streets between tall buildings.

Uncle Lee took Peter and Nancy to see the Dominion's Parliament Building with its stately

Peace Tower. In 1919 the then Prince of Wales laid the cornerstone. A great carillon, installed below the clock, played rich music. Uncle Lee said the smallest of the fifty-three bells weighed ten pounds, and the largest over 22,000 pounds.

Nancy was most impressed by the exquisite marble Altar of Remembrance in the Peace Tower, for it held the Book of Remembrance in which the names of all the Canadians who had lost their lives in the World War were inscribed.

Then early one morning the MacLarens took a train for Toronto, the second largest city of Canada.

"Toronto is the capital of the province of Ontario," Uncle Lee explained as he pointed out the fine government buildings, the famous university, and the beautiful homes with their lovely lake views.

But as Uncle Lee said, beauty alone could not make a city. Toronto owed its wealth to neighboring iron foundries, factories, and mines. Peter in his ramblings discovered a busy harbor and several meat-packing plants. With Uncle Lee, Nancy visited a factory where agricultural implements were manufactured and shipped by rail or water into the vast farming communities of Canada.

One evening after dinner, Uncle Lee got out his map and spread it on the table beside his dessert plate.

"This part of Ontario," he said, indicating the

Canadian Travel Bureau

THE PRINCE OF WALES ARCH IN TORONTO

south, "is called the Lake Peninsula. Most of the
people of Ontario live here, for it's an extension
of the plains of the United States, and, as you

know, the plains are very fertile. The people raise cattle, hogs, and fruit. The apple and peach orchards are wonderful to look at."

Nancy had not been paying much attention. Her eyes were on the little towns north of Toronto, and suddenly she put her finger on one of the names. Callander!

"Oh, I wish we could see the Dionne quintuplets!" she cried.

"We'll drive up there on Sunday," Uncle Lee promised. "There's an average of a thousand visitors every Sunday, but we may as well be part of the admiring throng."

On Sunday morning the procession of cars along the sandy stretch of good road leading into Callander told the world that the Dionne babies had made Dr. Allan Dafoe and their home town famous. To Peter and Nancy the procession seemed like a parade.

It was not hard to find the Dafoe Hospital, a one-story building with parking space for a thousand cars. Men, women, and children formed in groups about the strong fence that separated the world from the famous quintuplets.

Presently a nurse led the little girls out under the big umbrellas on the porch, and cries of delight ran through the crowd. Five little girls, all with big brown eyes and dark hair, chubby and eager! They played together gleefully, Yvonne, Annette, Cecile, Emilie, and Marie.

The MacLarens went on to Sudbury, north of

Georgian Bay, to visit the nickel mines. Peter and Nancy were amazed at the uses for nickel that Uncle Lee counted off: knives, forks, spoons, of course, and in addition, an alloy of nickel and steel was used for machinery, armor plates for warships, bridges, cars, and steel rails.

"Steel rails!" Uncle Lee emphasized the words, as they approached one of the big mines. "Steel rails, the most important use for nickel, have made Canada. Fifty-six thousand miles of steel have made communication and transportation possible for the great Dominion. And half the supply of the world's nickel is found right here in Sudbury."

The falls of a near-by river furnished the power that developed electricity for Sudbury, and it was a well-lighted mine into which the MacLarens descended. Nancy did not remain below long, but Peter stayed to watch the ore being mined.

He saw that it was handled in much the same way as coal and iron. The men broke great masses of the rock loose, loaded it on cars, and hoisted it to the surface.

From Sudbury, the MacLarens visited the gold fields at Timmins and Kirkland Lake. They marveled at all the immense machinery and the labor necessary to turn the rough ore from the mine into little oblong ingots of precious gold.

To get a taste of Canadian camp life, Uncle Lee, Peter, and Nancy, accompanied by a guide, went for a trip into the northern lake and bush country.

While Uncle Lee fished for trout and black bass, Peter and Nancy followed the trails with their guides. They learned to know the lynx, the otter, and the beaver and the marten. They became familiar with the honk of the Canadian goose, and they saw numerous birds which reminded them of home: martins, ruby-throated hummingbirds, finches, scarlet tanagers, great blue herons, and redheaded woodpeckers.

"Beyond those hills," Uncle Lee pointed out, "the rivers all flow north instead of south. Those hills are the watershed dividing the St. Lawrence waters from those of Hudson Bay."

One day the MacLarens saw a rider galloping along a distant hill. He wore riding breeches and a red coat.

"He is a Royal Canadian Mounted Policeman," Uncle Lee explained.

"So he's a real Mountie!" Peter exclaimed.

"The Mounties make up a unique police force," Uncle Lee continued. "They were organized years ago to bring law and order to the wild country of northwestern Canada where there were few towns and little or no established government. At first they were called the Northwest Mounted Police. In 1920 the force was reorganized as the Royal Canadian Mounted Police with headquarters at Ottawa.

"The Mounties have won the reputation of

Ewing Galloway
ROYAL CANADIAN MOUNTED POLICE

being one of the finest of the world's police forces. They now serve in any part of Canada. The force numbers about one thousand at the present time.

"The men live in barracks in the forest and spend many hours in the saddle. Their lives are often hazardous. The men must spend much of their time outdoors in all kinds of weather on errands of mercy or justice."

THE GREAT CANADIAN MOOSE

Ewing Galloway

FLOATING LOGS DOWN THE RIVER TO A SAWMILL

On the last morning of the camping trip Peter and Nancy came upon a great moose, just emerging from a cold, clear lake. He gave a startled look at the new-comers and crashed off into the brush.

Returning, the MacLarens had a better conception of what caused Toronto's prosperity. Many new homes had been built from money earned in northern Ontario. Some of it came from the mining of copper, gold, and nickel; some came from the furs produced; and some was earned in the lumbering industry.

WEST AND STILL FARTHER WEST

WESTWARD through the Great Lakes! The MacLarens were sailing through the Welland Canal into Lake Erie.

"Lake Ontario," Uncle Lee explained, as they paced the lake liner's deck, "is more than three hundred feet lower than Lake Erie. Niagara Falls covers 164 feet of this difference in one leap."

Peter and Nancy had already marveled at the swirling, plunging, green-blue water of Niagara. They could never forget the sight. They knew that Canada and the United States had agreed to use only part of Niagara's power so that the beauty of the falls might be preserved.

Most of the time while sailing through the lakes, the MacLarens could imagine that they were on the ocean, for often they were out of sight of land. Beyond the head of Lake Erie, however, the lake became narrower. The Detroit and St. Clair rivers, and Lake St. Clair became the waterways of the journey.

Then the MacLarens' boat sailed up Lake Huron, and finally at the northern end of Lake Huron the waterway narrowed into St. Mary's River. Here, Uncle Lee pointed out, the Soo Canal had been built so that ships might pass the rapids of the river and reach Lake Superior.

Canadian Travel Bureau

NIAGARA FALLS FROM THE CANADIAN SIDE

"Cities on both sides!" Peter cried. "One on the United States side, and one on the Canadian side."

"The twin cities of Sault Sainte Marie," Uncle Lee informed them.

"The locks interest me," Nancy remarked. "They open up like double doors. It's no trouble at all for our boat to go through. They are truly wonderful locks. Look, Peter."

Their steamer crossed deep, cold Lake Superior and brought the travelers at last to those other twin cities, Fort William and Port Arthur, where they gazed in astonishment at the biggest grain elevators in the world. Here was a new

Canadian Travel Bureau

PORTAGE AVENUE IN WINNIPEG

kind of wealth—the western treasury of wheat!

By train they continued the journey on through the Lake of the Woods region toward Winnipeg. The name had the magic sound of far places for Nancy. Once she and Peter had visited a family in Winnipeg, Manitoba's capital city and the gateway to the great wheat belt, but she had been too young to remember much about it. Since then it had grown to be Canada's largest Middle Western city.

Peter and Nancy were amazed at the size of Winnipeg with its broad streets and avenues bordered by fine residences and great office buildings.

"Skyscrapers!" Peter exclaimed.

It seemed strange to meet trappers, ranchers, miners, and farmers on the streets in such a great city. The MacLarens fell in love all over again with the friendliness of the West.

"Winnipeg is a great railway center," said Uncle Lee. "It's the great junction for all the lines west, east, south, and even as far north now as Churchill, right on Hudson Bay. In fact, Manitoba now has an Atlantic port of its own at Churchill, from which ships carry western grain to Europe. Churchill is actually nearer to Liverpool than Montreal is, but of course the Hudson Bay route is open for only a few weeks in the year because of ice."

The Winnipeg shops were filled with fine blankets and sports outfits, and Nancy picked out some of that beautiful English china, Crown Derby, for her mother.

By train, a very modern train indeed, the MacLarens rode on into Saskatchewan, making a stop at Regina, the capital city. The wheat fields were golden in the sunlight. Uncle Lee said that Saskatchewan was known as the hard-wheat country.

"This wheat land is one vast block of grain," he explained. "No matter in which direction you traveled, north, east, south, or west, you would still be in a grain field, probably for days."

Canadian Travel Bureau

A HIGHWAY IN SASKATCHEWAN

Regina and Saskatoon proved to be prosperous cities, for the Canadian pioneer adventurer had now become a substantial farmer.

Beyond the wheat country, Uncle Lee said, lay a large forest belt, with its menaces of muskeg and forest fires. There was little saw timber, but perhaps a fourth of the timber growth would do for pulpwood. In this bush country horses and cattle were raised. The farmers had plenty of feed for the horses, including wild hay. There was enough wood for winter fires, and in the south farmers had peat coal or lignite which they could dig up in their own fields. In Wyoming, Peter had once seen his uncle dig lignite. It looked like dirt but burned like coal. He thought wistfully of the somewhat smoky but good fire it had made in the Klondike stove of the shack.

The train carried the MacLarens on into Alberta toward Edmonton, its capital city, and the gateway to the Peace River country and the Mackenzie basin.

"Manitoba, Saskatchewan, and Alberta are called the Prairie Provinces," Uncle Lee told them.

From the car windows Peter and Nancy again saw the yellow sea of wheat which seemed to stretch all the way from Manitoba. The slightest wind ruffled it into waves like those of a sea on which a brilliant golden sun was setting. The only break in the gold was an occasional pasture, still green from the late summer rains.

"Beyond the grain fields lies wooded land," Uncle Lee observed. "I'd like to arrange a trip north if school didn't start so soon."

Such a deluge of questions followed that Uncle Lee sank back. A big fellow wearing a ten-gallon hat and shiny boots that intrigued Peter sat near them. He came over and spoke to Uncle Lee.

"Do you mind if I relieve you, sir, of answering those questions?"

At Uncle Lee's invitation he seated himself beside Peter, facing Uncle Lee and Nancy.

"Whitcomb's my name," he began. "Sam Whitcomb. I've got a ranch up in the Peace River country. So you want to know all about Alberta? Well, I came in here when Edmonton was a tiny settlement and you washed in a tin basin. But the good land was here waiting, over two hundred thousand square acres of it, with plenty of rainfall and snow, and a couple of thousand hours of sunshine a year. It does run forty and fifty below sometimes out where I live, but the mean temperature for Alberta is thirty-seven degrees. Besides, the sunshine makes up for the low temperatures, and a fellow doesn't mind cold in dry air the way he would if it were muggy."

"Would there be room for some fellows like me?" Peter inquired.

"Room?" Mr. Whitcomb laughed. "Room? With a population of less than eight hundred thousand? There's room all right, and opportunity at any door you care to open. We've got seventy million acres of land suitable for agriculture and only eighteen million acres cultivated thus far. There are one million tons in coal reserves. You can take your choice—lignite, bituminous, or subbituminous. About 65 per cent of gas consumption in Canada is natural gas. The principal fields are at Turner Valley, Medicine Hat, Viking, and Foremost. Are you interested in petroleum?"

"Yes, sir," Peter answered. "I guess everybody is interested in oil."

"Well, we've got oil fields at Turner Valley, Red Coulée, Wainwright, Ribstone, and Skiff. There are 120 wells thus far, and the annual production is around 1,300,000 barrels, believe it or not! And, if the oil business doesn't appeal to you, we've still got sixty thousand square miles of timber, fifteen thousand square miles of bituminous land, fields of clay west of Edmonton, salt at Fort McMurray, fur farms, fisheries, and good facilities for aviation. One of the finest airports you'll find anywhere is right in Edmonton."

"I'm interested," Peter said. "But I haven't finished school as yet."

"School?" The Canadian was almost impatient. "We can take care of that. We have over four thousand primary and high schools in Alberta right now. Then there are three normal schools, a technical school, a couple of agricultural colleges, and our fine modern university with five affiliated colleges. If you can get through a few of them, you'll be what the world calls educated!"

Uncle Lee interrupted the friendly informant to ask about the fishing in Alberta. He was promised the best pike, perch, and pickerel should he fish in the Rocky Mountain streams, and the finest in trout should he choose the little streams in the foothills.

Mr. Whitcomb spoke, too, of wild life in the Banff National Park and added that he usually carried a camera when visiting the park. From

Canadian Travel Bureau

BEARS IN JASPER NATIONAL PARK

his vest pocket he drew out a folder containing
pictures he had taken and passed them around
to Nancy, Uncle Lee, and Peter. There were
two bighorn sheep climbing a steep cliff. A pair
of mountain goats were coming gingerly down
a steep, rocky pass. Caribou, elk, and moose fed
in some clearings. A deer and a doe had come to
drink at a brook. A grizzly bear stood in a mountain road. A black bear pawed honey from a
hollow tree. A mule deer lifted its large ears as
if listening, and a pair of antelope with gentle
eyes paused in a meadow. As the Canadian
talked, the MacLarens saw wild ducks and geese
fly up out of the wild rice, and sharp-tailed

BIGHORN SHEEP IN BANFF NATIONAL PARK

grouse, ruffed grouse, spruce grouse, and ptarmigan flew away with a drumming of wings. Hungarian pheasants, Chinese, and Mongolian pheasants preened their colorful feathers as they strutted in the sun.

"Edmonton!" called the conductor, and the pictures of the Canadian wilds had to be returned to their owner. The MacLarens thanked Mr. Whitcomb and promised to visit his ranch some day.

Edmonton was undoubtedly a busy traffic center for northern fur traders, farmers, and miners, but it was also a very beautiful city worthy of tourist trade. The handsome parliament buildings and the equally handsome Alberta University were as imposing as any the MacLarens had seen.

Located as it is on a tableland above the north Saskatchewan river, the city boasted a splendid view. Below lay the winding river, the green valley, and the vast plains beyond. The hotel was so luxurious that Peter rebelled.

"I thought out here we might stay in a log cabin inn," he objected as Uncle Lee registered.

"You're about fifty years too late, son," a Canadian Mountie in a red jacket informed Peter.

Early in the morning the MacLarens left Edmonton for Calgary, due south. As the trade center for all the ranchers in the vicinity, Calgary was quite as busy as Edmonton.

"Calgary owes its growth to the Canadian Pacific Railway," Uncle Lee informed Peter and

James Sawders

GRAIN ELEVATORS ON THE PRAIRIE

Nancy. "Probably some of the prosperity is due to the fine brown sandstone near by. You'll notice that a good many of the buildings are made of this sandstone."

"Anyone could guess from the grain elevators we have seen that wheat is the most important agricultural product in the province of Alberta," remarked Peter, as yet another one came into view.

The few hours in Calgary assuredly were not enough, and the trip into the busy oil fields and the southern coal area was all too brief. Soon the MacLaren party were westbound again, this time for Banff and Lake Louise. This would be their first experience in the Canadian Rockies.

That westward trip was a series of wonderful pictures in color. While Nancy exclaimed at snow-crowned mountains, Peter would point out an icy river grinding its way through a deep chasm. Or, while Peter was shouting at the sight of a forested slope in whose trees the hoarfrost hung like white blossoms, Nancy was exclaiming over a tiny mountain lake, blue-green and shining like a jewel.

Banff, just eighty miles westward from Calgary, needed nothing more than its magnificent scenery to win it acclaim. In this region among great glaciers, imposing mountains, and blue lakes, the traveler could enjoy life to the full. Here were tame bears, deer, and mountain goats. The great Banff Springs Hotel, overlooking the Bow River valley, was quite the most luxurious hotel the children had ever seen.

The MacLarens were prepared for their first glimpse of Lake Louise, a glorious lake walled in by mountain peaks and forests, the finest gem of Rocky Mountain Park.

From Lake Louise the train took the MacLarens westward and southward through the impressive Canadian Rockies. Uncle Lee told the children that the province of British Columbia was largely mountainous, only the narrow seacoast being low or level.

Finally the American travelers arrived at Van-

Ewing Galloway

BEAUTIFUL LAKE LOUISE

Canadian Travel Bureau

BOW FALLS IN BANFF NATIONAL PARK

couver, the great western port, a fine Canadian city only a few hours' trip north of their own city of Seattle in the state of Washington.

Uncle Lee explained that though Prince Rupert, much farther up the coast, was an important shipping center, Vancouver, the largest city in British Columbia and one of the largest in all Canada, was the main Pacific port.

"To this large and well-protected harbor," he added, "come ships from all the countries of the Orient and even from Europe by way of the Panama Canal. Canada exports meat, grain, fruit,

Ewing Galloway

THE CITY OF VICTORIA AND HARBOR

and lumber in great quantities, and it is at Vancouver that much of this produce is loaded on the waiting ships. Passenger ships dock at Vancouver too, the ships coming mainly from China, Japan, Australia, and the Hawaiian Islands."

After Peter and Nancy had seen Vancouver's well-constructed public buildings, gone swimming at one of the beaches, and remarked a great many times about the freshness of the grass and the abundance of flowers, they and Uncle Lee paid a visit to Victoria, the capital of British Columbia.

Peter and Nancy had been anxious to see Victoria and Vancouver Island on which Victoria is located. They were interested to learn that Vancouver Island is almost as large as the whole of Ireland. A fast motor ferry took the MacLarens quickly and comfortably to the beautiful old-world city.

"How much like England all of this is!" Uncle Lee kept repeating. "How much like England and London!"

Peter and Nancy visited the Parliament Buildings, saw the statue of Queen Victoria, and browsed in curio and antique shops. One of their happiest experiences was a cycling trip they took one afternoon.

The MacLaren children said good-by to Canada at Vancouver in a park overlooking the harbor and the straits leading out into the Pacific. Uncle Lee had arranged for a car for the trip back to the United States and home, and while they waited for it Peter and Nancy strolled in the park. They stood looking at the statue in honor of Warren Gamaliel Harding.

Nancy stared up at the two great female figures that represented the United States and Canada. They faced each other, each with a hand on the laurel wreath between them. Then she read the inscription carved on the granite slab below, glancing from time to time at the face of the president carved in relief between the blocks of inscription.

"Canada hopes that our country and hers will always be friends," she reported to Peter. "She hopes that there will never be armed guards at the border and that the peace that now exists will never be broken."

"I should hope not!" Peter was serious. "Imagine quarreling with a grand country like Canada!"

Then Uncle Lee appeared with the car, ready to drive down into Washington. Thus it was that Peter and Nancy passed through the famous wooden gate and the uncut weeds. Above the gate the words, MAY THESE GATES NEVER BE CLOSED, expressed all that was in their hearts.

PRONOUNCING VOCABULARY

PRONOUNCING VOCABULARY

KEY: ā as āte; ȧ as vȧcation; â as câre; ă as ădd; ä as ärm; ȧ as ȧsk;
ē as ēve; ĕ as ĕvent; ȇ as ȇnd; ē as makēr; ī as īce; ĭ as ĭll; N as a nasal ng;
ng as sing; ō as ōld; ŏ as ŏbey; ô as fôr; ŏ as ŏdd; oi as oil; o͞o as fo͞od;
o͝o as fo͝ot; ou as out; th as in the; ū as cūbe; û as ûnite; û as fûr; ŭ as ŭp;
ü as menü; zh as z in azure.

Abraham (ā′brȧ-hăm)
Acadia (ȧ-kā′dĭ-ȧ)
Acadian (ȧ-kā′dĭ-ăn)
adiós (ä-dyōs′)
Adirondack (ăd′ĭ-rŏn′dăk)
Agua (ä′gwä)
aguamiel (ä′gwä-myĕl′)
ahuehuete (ä′wä-wä′tȧ)
Alaska (ȧ-lăs′kȧ)
Alberta (ăl-bûr′tȧ)
Alvarado, Pedro de (äl′vä-rä′thō,
pä′drō dā)
Amapala (ä′mä-pä′lä)
Amatitlán (ä-mä′tĕ-tlän′)
Amecameca (ä-mä′kä-mä′kä)
Anáhuac (ä-nä′wäk)
Ancón (äng-kōn′)
Annapolis (ă-năp′ō-lĭs)
Annapolis Royal (ă-năp′ō-lĭs roi′ăl)
Anticosti (ăn′tĭ-kŏs′tĭ)
Antigua (ăn-tē′gwä)
Antilles (ăn-tĭl′ēz)
Appalachian (ăp′ȧ-lăch′ĭ-ăn)
Argentine (är′jĕn-tēn)
Arvida (är-vī′dȧ)
Asia (ā′zhȧ)
Asunción (ä-so͞on′syōn′)
Atitlán (ä′tĕ-tlän′)
Australia (ôs-trāl′yȧ)
Avenue des Braves (ȧ-vĕ-no͞o dä
bräv′)
Aztec (ăz′tĕk)

Bahamas (bȧ-hä′mȧz)
Baie Comeau (bā′ kô′mō′)

Balboa (băl-bō′ȧ)
Banff (bămf)
Basilica (bȧ-sĭl′ĭ-kȧ)
Belanger (bĕ-läN′zhä′)
Benares (bĕ-nä′rĕz)
Bering (bēr′ĭng)
Bonapart, Napoleon (bō′nȧ-pärt,
nȧ-pō′lĕ-ŭn)
Borda (bôr′dȧ′)
Borde, Joseph le (bôrd, zhō-sĕf′ lĕ)
Boucher (bo͞o′shä′)
bougainvillea (bo͞o′gĭn-vĭl′ĕ-ȧ)
Bras d'Or (brä′ dôr′)
Brazil (brȧ-zĭl′)
British Columbia (brĭt′ĭsh kō-lŭm′-
bĭ-ȧ)
brujo (bro͞o′hō)

Cabot (kăb′ŭt)
calèche (kȧ′lĕsh′)
Calgary (kăl′gȧ-rĭ)
Callander (kăl′ȧn-dēr)
Campeche (käm-pā′chȧ)
Canada (kăn′ȧ-dȧ)
Canadian (kȧ-nā′dĭ-ăn)
Canal del Desagüe (kä-näl′ dĕl
dĕs-ä′gwä)
Cape Breton (kāp brĭt′ŭn)
Cardenas (kär′dä-näs)
Carib (kăr′ĭb)
Caribbean (kăr′ĭ-bē′ăn)
Carlotta (kär-lŏt′ȧ)
Carranza (kär-rän′sä)
Cartago (kär-tä′gō)
Cartier Jaques (kȧr′tyä′, zhȧk)

312

Catorce (kä-tôr'sā)
cenote (så-nō'tå)
Cenote de Xtoloc (så-nō'tå dä shtō-lŏk')
Cenote Sagrado (så-nō'tå sä-grä'dō)
Cerro del Carmen (sĕr'rō dĕl kär'mĕn)
Cervantes (thĕr-vän'tās)
Chagres (chä'grĕs)
chalupa (chä-lōō'pä)
Champlain (shăm'plān')
Chapala (chä-pä'lä)
Chapultepec (chä-pōōl'tå-pĕk')
Charlottetown (shär'lŏt-toun)
Château de Ramezay (shä'tō' dē rä-mĕ-zā')
Château Frontenac (shä'tō frŏn't'-näk')
Chaudière (shō'dyâr')
chayote (chä-yō'tå)
Cheops (kē'ŏps)
Chichen Itzá (chĕ-chĕn'ēt-sä')
chicle (chē'k'l)
chili con carne (chē'lå kŏn kär'nå)
China (chī'nå)
Cholula (chŏ-lōō'lä)
Chucunaque (shōō-kōō-nä'kä)
Churchill (chûrch'ĭl)
Churubusco (chōō'rōō-bōōs'kō)
Cimarron (sē'mär-rŏn')
Cinco de Mayo (sēn'kō dä mä'yō)
Citadel (sĭt'å-dĕl)
Ciudad Trujillo (syōō-thäth' trōō-hēl'yō)
Ciudad Victoria (syōō-thäth' vēk-tō'rē-ä)
Coatepeque (kŏ-ä'tå-pā'kå)
Colombia (kŏ-lŏm'bĕ-ä)
Colonia (kŏ-lō'nyä)
Comayagua (kō'mä-yä'gwä)
cordillera (kôr'dĭl-yâr'å)
Córdoba (kôr'dŏ-vä)
Corinto (kŏ-rēn'tō)
Cortez (kôr'tĕz)
Cosegüina (kō'så-gwē'nå)

Costa Rica (kŏs'tå rē'kå)
Costa Rican (kŏs'tå rē'kăn)
Cote (kōt)
Cote de la Montagne (kōt dē là môn'tån'y')
Cristobal (krĭs-tō'băl)
Cuba (kū'bá)
Cuban (kū'băn)
Cuernavaca (kwĕr'nä-vä'kä)
Cuilapan (kwē-lä'pän)
Cunard, Samuel (kû-närd', săm'-û-ĕl)

Darien (dâr'ĭ-ĕn')
Desierto de los Leones (dä-sē-ĕr'tō dä lōs lā-ō'nās)
Diaz, Porfirio (dē'äs, pōr-fē'rē-ō)
Diego (dyä'gō)
Diego, Juan (dyä'gō, hwän')
Dionne (dyōn)
Dominican Republic (dŏ-mĭn'ĭ-kăn rĕ-pŭb'lĭk)
duenna (dû-ĕn'á)
Dufferin Terrace (dŭf'ĕr-ĭn tĕr'ĭs)

Edmonton (ĕd'mŭn-tŭn)
Egypt (ē'jĭpt)
El Camino Real (ĕl kä-mē'nō râ-äl')
El Carmen (ĕl kär'mĕn)
El Castillo (ĕl käs-tēl'yō)
El Real (ĕl râ-äl')
enchilada (ĕn'chĕ-lä'dä)
Erie (ēr'ĭ)
Estados Unidos Mexicanos (ĕs-tä'-dōs ōō-nē'dōs mĕk-sē-kä'nōs)
Eternity (ē-tûr'nĭ-tĭ)
European (ū'rŏ-pē'ăn)
Evangeline (ē-văn'jĕ-lēn)
evangelista (ē-vän-hĕ-lĭs'tä)

Fonseca (fŏn-sā'kä)
Fort-de-France (fôr' dē-fräns')
Franco-Latin (frăng'kŏ-lăt'ĭn)
Fredericton (frĕd'ĕr-ĭk-tŭn)
Fuego (fwä'gō)
Fundy (fŭn'dĭ)

Gaillard (gāl'ērd)
Galicia (gá-lĭsh'ĭ-á)
Gálvez (gäl'väth)
Gaspé (gäs'pā')
Gatun (gä-tōōn')
Georgian (jôr'jĭ-ăn)
Goethals (gō'thălz)
Goethe (gû'tĕ)
Great Britain (grāt brĭt'ĕn)
Grenfell (grĕn'fĕl)
gringo (grĭng'gō)
Gringolandia (grĭng'gō-lăn'dĭ-á)
Guadalajara (gwä'thä-lä-hä'rä)
Guadalupe (gwä'thä-lōō'pä)
Guanajuato (gwä'nä-hwä'tō)
guaraches (gwä-rä'chäs)
Guatemala (gwä'tá-mä'lä)
Guatemalan (gwä'tá-mä'lăn)
guayule (gwä-yōō'lä)

hacienda (ä-syĕn'dä)
Haiti (hā'tĭ)
Haitian (hā'tĭ-ăn)
Halifax (hăl'ĭ-făks)
Harding, Warren Gamaliel (här'-
    dĭng, wŏr'ĕn gá-mā'lĭ-ĕl)
Havana (há-văn'á)
Hawaiian (hä-wī'yăn)
Hébert, Louis (ā'bâr', lōō'ē')
henequen (hĕn'ĕ-kĕn)
Hindu (hĭn'dōō)
Hispaniola (hĭs'păn-yō'lá)
Homer (hō'mēr)
Honduras (hŏn-dōō'räs)
Hôtel de Ville (ō-tĕl' dē vēl')
huipil (wĕ-pēl')
Huron (hū'rŏn)

iguana (ĭ-gwä'ná)
Indies (ĭn'dĭz)
Irapuato (ē'rä-pwä'tō)
Irazu (ē'rä-sōō')
Ireland (īr'lănd)
Iturbide (ē'tōōr-bē'thä)
Ixtacihuatl (ēs'tä-sē'wät'l)
Izalco (ĕ-säl'kō)

Jalisco (hä-lēs'kō)
Jamaica (já-mā'ká)
Japan (já-păn')
Jaracuaro (hwä-rä-kwä'rō)
Jasper (jăs'pēr)
Juachitan (hwä-chē'tán)
Jerusalem (jĕ-rōō'sá-lĕm)
Josephine (jō'zĕ-fēn)
Juarez, Benito (hwä'räs, bĕ-nē'tō)
jute (jōōt)

Kakichecial (kä-kē-chäs-yäl')
Kirkland (kûrk'lănd)
Klondike (klŏn'dīk)

Labrador (lăb'rá-dôr')
Lachine (lá-shēn')
Lago (lä'gō)
Langlois (läɴ'glwä')
Laredo (lá-rā'dō)
Laurentian (lô-rĕn'shĭ-ăn)
Laval (lá'văl')
leche (lä'chä)
León (lá-ōn')
Lesseps, Ferdinand de (lĕ'sĕps',
    fûr'dĭ-nănd dē)
Lévis (lä'vē')
Limón (lē-mōn')
Liverpool (lĭv'ēr-pōōl)
London (lŭn'dŭn)
Louisburg (lōō'ĭs-bûrg)
Louise (lōō-ēz')

Mackenzie (má-kĕn'zĭ)
Madam (măd'ăm)
Madero (mä-thā'rō)
Magdalens (măg'dá-lĕnz)
maguey (măg'wä)
Malecon (mä-lä'kôn)
Malinche (mä-lēn'chä)
Malinzín (mä'lēn-tsēn')
Maltrata (măl-trä'tä)
Managua (mä-nä'gwä)
Manitoba (măn'ĭ-tō'bá)
Manoir Richelieu (mă-nwä rē'shē-
    lyû')

mantilla (măn-tĭl′à)
Mariscal (mär-rēs-käl′)
Mariscala (mäh-rēs-kä′lä)
Martinique (mär′tĭ-nēk′)
Matapedia (má-tä-pēd′ē-á)
matte (măt)
Maximilian (măk′sĭ-mĭl′ĭ-ăn)
Maya (mä′yà)
Mayan (mä′yăn)
Mazatlán (mä′sä-tlän′)
Mecca (mĕk′à)
Mercado Central (mĕr-kä′dō sän-
träl′)
Merced (mēr-sĕd′)
Mérida (mä′rĕ-ŧhä)
mesa (mē′sä)
mesquite (mĕs-kēt′)
Mexican (mĕk′sĭ-kăn)
Mexico (mĕk′sĭ-kō)
Michoacán (mĕ-chō′ä-kän′)
Minas Basin (mĭ′năs bā′s′n)
Minerva (mĭ-nûr′và)
Miraflores (mē′rä-flō′räs)
Miskito (mĭs-kē′tō)
Mitla (mēt′lä)
Mixtec (mĭks′tĕk)
Moncton (mŭngk′t′n)
Mongolian (mŏng-gō′lĭ-ăn)
Monsieur (mē-syû′)
Montcalm (mŏnt-käm′)
Monte de Piedad (mon′tä dä pyä-
ŧhäŧh′)
Monterrey (mōn′tēr-rā′)
Montezuma (mŏn′tĕ-zoō′má)
Montmorency (mŏnt′mŏ-rĕn′sĭ)
Montreal (mŏnt′rĕ-ôl′)
Moor (moōr)
Morelos (mŏ-rä′lōs)
Mormon (môr′mŭn)
morrales (mŏ-rä′läs)
Morro (mŏr′rō)
Motagua (mŏ-tä′gwä)
mozo (mō′thō)
Mudejar (moō-ŧhä′här)
Murillo (mû-rĭl′ō)

Nassau (năs′ô)
Nevado de Toluca (nä-vä′dō dä
tŏ-loō′kä)
New Brunswick (nū brŭnz′wĭk)
Newfoundland (nū′fŭnd-lǎnd′)
Niagara (nī-ăg′á-rá)
Nicaragua (nĭk′á-rä′gwà)
noches buenas (nō′chås bwä′näs)
norte (nôr′tä)
Northumberland Strait (nôr-thŭm′-
bēr-lănd strät)
Norway (nôr′wä)
Nova Scotia (nō′vá skō′shà)
Nuevo Laredo (nwä′vō lä-rä′dō)

Oaxaco (wä-hä′kä)
Obregón (ŏ′brä-gōn′)
Olas Atlas (ō′läs ăt′läs)
Ontario (ŏn-târ′ĭ-ō)
Orizaba (ō′rĕ-sä′bä)
Orleans (ôr′lĕ-ănz)
Otomi (ŏ-tō′mĭ)
Ottawa (ŏt′á-wá)

Pahuatlan (pä-hwä′tlän)
Panama (păn′á-mä′)
Panduro (pän-doō′rō)
papaya (pä-pä′yä)
Paraguay (păr′á-gwä)
patio (pä′tyō)
Pátzcuaro (päs′kwä-rō)
Pedro Miguel (pä′drō mĕ-gĕl′)
Pelée (pē-lā′)
peon (pē′ŏn)
peso (pä′sō)
Picacho (pē-kä′chō)
Pinguico (pĭng-gwē′kō)
piragua (pĭ-rä′gwà)
Plato (plä′tō)
plaza (plä′zä)
Plaza de la Constitución (plä′zä dä
lä kōn-stē-toō-sēōn′)
Plaza Zenea (plä′zä zĕn-ē′á)
Pompeii (pŏm-pā′yē)
Ponce (pōn′sä)

ponchos (pŏn′chōz)
Popocatepetl (pŏ-pō′kä-tä′pĕt′l)
Portage (pôr-tázh′)
Portal de las Flores (pōr-täl′ dä läs
   flō′räs)
portales (pôr-tä′läs)
Port-au-Prince (pôr′-tō′prăns′)
Port la Joie (pōr lȧ jwä′)
Port Royal (pōrt roi′ăl)
Prado (prä′thō)
Prince Rupert (prĭns rōō′pĕrt)
Progreso (prŏ-grä′sō)
Puebla (pwä′blä)
Puerto Barrios (pwĕr′tō bär′rĕ-ōs)
Puerto Cortés (pwĕr′tō kŏr-tās′)
Puerto Rican (pwĕr′tō rē′kăn)
Puerto Rico (pwĕr′tō rē′kō)
pulque (pōōl′kȧ)

Quai du Roi (kä dü rwä′)
Querétaro (kȧ-rā′tä-rō)
Quetzalcoatl (kĕt-säl′kŏ-ä′t′l)
Quezaltenango (kȧ-säl′tȧ-näng′gō)
Quintana Roo (kĕn-tä′nä rō′ō)
Quiriguá (kē′rĕ-gwä′)
Quixote (kĕ-hō′tȧ)

rebozo (rȧ-bō′sō)
Red Coulée (red kōō-lā′)
Regina (rĕ-jī′nȧ)
Richelieu (rē′shĕ-lyû′)
Rideau (rē′dō′)
Rimouski (rĕ-mōōs′kĕ)
Rio Cupatitzio (rē′ō kōō-pȧ-tĕt-
   sē′ō)
Rio Grande (rē′ō grän′dä)
Rivera, Diego (rĕ-vä′rä, dyä′gō)
Rosario (rŏ-sä′rĕ-ō)
Rosetta (rŏ-zĕt′ȧ)
Rubens (rōō′bĕnz)
Rue de Notre Dame (rü′ dĕ nô′tr′
   dȧm′)
Rul, Conde de (rōōl, kōn′dȧ dä)

Sacro Monte (sä′krō mon′tȧ)
Saguenay (săg′ĕ-nä′)

St. Clair (sȧnt klâr′)
Ste. Anne de Beaupré (sȧnt ăn dē
   bō′prä′)
Saltillo (säl-tēl′yō)
Salvador (säl′vä-dōr′)
San Cayetano (sän kä-yä-tän′ō)
San Francisco (săn frăn-sĭs′kō)
San José (sän hŏ-sä′)
San Juan (sän hwän′)
San Juancito (sän hwän-sē′tō)
San Juan del Norte (sän hwän′ dĕl
   nôr′tȧ)
San Juan Teotihuacan (sän hwän′
   tä′ŏ-tē′wä-kän′)
San Luis Potosí (sän′ lōō-ēs pō′-
   tŏ-sē′)
San Miguel (sän mē-gĕl′)
San Salvador (sän säl′vä-dôr′)
Santa Lucrecia (sän′tä lū-krä′syä)
Santa Rosa (sän′tä rō′sä)
Santo Domingo (sän′tō dŏ-mĭng′gō)
Saskatchewan (săs-kăch′ĕ-wŏn)
Saskatoon (săs′kȧ-tōōn′)
Sault Sainte Marie (sōō sȧnt mȧ-rē′)
señorita (sā′nyŏ-rē′tä)
Septiembre (sĕp-tĕ-ĕm′brä)
serape (sĕ-rä′pä)
Seville (sĕv′ĭl)
Sierra Madre (sĭ-ĕr′ȧ mä′drä)
siesta (sĭ-ĕs′tȧ)
sisal (sī′säl)
sombrero (sŏm-brä′rō)
Soo (sōō)
Sorel (sō-rĕl′)
Sous le Fort (sōō lĕ fōr′)
Sudbury (sŭd′bĕr′ĭ)
Suez (sōō-ĕz′)
Superior (sṳ-pēr′ĭ-ēr)
Sydney (sĭd′nĭ)

Tadoussac (tȧ′dōō′sȧk′)
Tajo de Nochistongo (tä′zhō dä
   nō-chēs-tŏn′gō)
tamale (tȧ-mä′lĕ)
Tamaulipas (tä-mä′ōō-lē′päs)

Tampico (täm-pē′kō)
Tarascan (tä-räs′kăn)
Tartar (tär′tēr)
Taxco (tăs′kō)
Tegucigalpa (tä-gōō′sê-gäl′pä)
Tehuantepec (tâ-wän′tâ-pĕk′)
Temollin (tā-mō′yĭn)
Tenochtitlan (tâ-nōch′tê-tlän′)
teocalli (tē′ô-kăl′ē)
Teotihuacan (tä′ô-tē′wä-kän′)
Teotitlan (tä-ō-tê′tlän)
Tepeyac (tä-pä′yäk)
Texcoco (täs-kō′kō)
Thetford (thĕt′fērd)
Thorold (thō′rōld)
Timmins (tĭm′ĭnz)
Tlaloc (tlä-lōk′)
Tlascalan (tläs-kä′lăn)
Tlaxcala (tläs-kä′lä)
Toltec (tôl′tĕk)
Toluca (tô-lōō′kä)
Toronto (tô-rŏn′tō)
tortilla (tôr-tē′yä)
Trinidad (trē′nĕ-thäth′)
Trinity (trĭn′ĭ-tĭ)
Trujillo (trōō-hēl′yō)
Tudor (tū′dēr)
Tula (tōō′lä)

Tule (tōō′lĕ)
Turia (tōō-rē′-ä)

Uruapan (ōō′rōō-ä′pän)
Uxmal (ōōz-mäl′)

Valbuena (väl-bwä′nä)
Vancouver (văn-kōō′vēr)
vaquero (vä-kä′rō)
Venice (vĕn′ĭs)
Veracruz (vä′rä krōōs′)
Veta Madre (vä′tä mä′drå)
Victoria (vĭk-tō′rĭ-á)
Viga (vē′gä)
Virgin (vûr′jĭn)
volador (vō′lä-thôr′)

Wainwright (wān′rīt)
Wales (wālz)
Welland (wĕl′ånd)
Winnipeg (wĭn′ĭ-pĕg)
Wolfe (wŏŏlf)

Xochimilco (hō′chê-mēl′kō)

Yucatán (yōō′kä-tän′)

Zapotec (sä′pô-tĕk′)
Zararacua (zä-rä-rä-kōō′ä)
Zócalo (sō′kä-lō)